The Sussex Tree Book

Owen Johnson

To my Mother and Father,
who first developed my interest in trees

Front cover: The author inside the Queen Elizabeth Oak at Cowdray Park; title page: the largest and finest Hungarian Oak in Britain, at Buxted Park; below: the ancient Judas Tree in Worthing Crematorium; back cover (left to right): *Stuartia sinensis* in Tilgate Park, aspens at Mayfield and broad-leaved limes at Clayton Holt.

ISBN: 0 9533493 0 6

Published by Pomegranate Press, Church Cottage, Westmeston, Sussex BN6 8RH

British Library Cataloguing-in-Publication Data.
A catalogue record for this book is available from the British Library

Printed by Ghyllprint, Ghyll Industrial Estate, Heathfield, East Sussex TN21 8AW

Contents

Measuring the diameter of the Wellingtonia at Rocks Park School, Uckfield, one of the biggest trees in Britain.

Introduction

*P*erhaps the best panorama of Sussex is the one from Ditchling Beacon. You can see the sea, sweeping in a broad curve round the south of the county. You can look, in either direction, along the sculpted crests of the South Downs; beneath you is the plain of the Weald, and the Forest Ridges rise to the north. You can see the tower-blocks of down-town Brighton, the mellow roofs of Ditchling, church-spires, stuccoed mansions, factories and pylons. You can see green lanes, winding roads and bypasses. You can see blazes of oilseed rape, or wide ploughlands, or thistly paddocks. And, everywhere, you can see trees: the down-land shelterbelts and roundels of the Stanmer estate; gale-clipped thorns on the open downs; the field oaks and coppices of the Low Weald, seeming to merge into one wide forest; cottage cherries and yellow cypresses; street trees among the rooftops; silvery willows marking the rivers; poplar belts and pine plantations; the distant towers of wellingtonias.

A view along the flanks of the Downs at Ditchling Beacon.

Trees, surely, contribute as much as any landscape feature to the environment we live in. In fact, when we visualise a familiar scene, what we think of is the landform plus its tree-cover: Chanctonbury Hill with its broken ring of beeches, Black Down crowned with its dark serration of pines. Yet, for all the impact of trees on our imaginations and our surroundings, the most basic of questions remain to be asked and answered. Which are the trees people are planting most? Which grow biggest, and where? How many different kinds are there in Sussex, and are these the same as there were a century ago? Or are some about to go extinct here? Is Sussex a good place to look for some of the world's rarest species, and, if so, are these likely to be found in one or two famous collections, or here, there and everywhere?

The trees all around had begun to fascinate me in my early teens. Opposite our home in St Leonards was a public gardens, Alexandra Park, which, I quickly discovered, seemed to contain most of the kinds of trees which were described in Alan Mitchell's *Field Guide to the Trees of Britain and Northern Europe*, plus quite a few which weren't. And, three kilometres away, Beauport Park, an overgrown private estate, seemed to offer endless opportunities for a teenager to crash through rampant rhododendrons and suddenly encounter the buttresses of giant conifers, or strange, huge leaves. I was particularly lucky: Alexandra Park is one of the nation's finest public tree collections, but in 1980 had yet to be 'discovered' by Mitchell himself; Beauport - a celebrated collection until the thirties - was too vast and too tangled for anyone to have more than scratched the surface.

Collins, 1974. Probably still the best available field guide to British trees

The first attempts to locate the biggest and rarest trees in Britain were largely motivated by the search for new timber species, and culminated in J. C. Elwes' and Augustine Henry's monumental *Trees of Great Britain and Ireland* in 1906-1913. The late Alan Mitchell, whose eloquence and enthusiasm first inspired my own interest in trees and that of many others, had a similar remit with the Forestry Commission in the 1950s, but his records of timber conifers soon spilled over into an obsession with measuring all the finest trees in parks and gardens across the country. In 1988 his life's work became the basis of a registered charity, the Tree Register of the British Isles (TROBI).

Privately printed; facsimile edition by the Royal Forestry Society, 1972

Metres	Feet	Cm Diam.	Feet Girth
0	0	0	0
1		10	1
2		20	2
3	10	30	3
4		40	4
5		50	5
6	20	60	6
7			
8		70	7
9	30	80	8
10		90	9
11		100	10
12	40	110	11
13		120	12
14		130	13
15	50	140	14
16		150	15
17		160	16
18	60	170	17
19		180	18
20		190	19
21	70	200	20
22		210	21
23		220	22
24	80	230	23
25		240	24
26		250	25
27	90	260	26
28		270	27
29		280	28
30	100	290	29
31		300	30
32		310	31
33		320	32
34	110	330	33
35		340	34
36		350	35
37	120	360	36
38		370	37
39		380	38
40	130	390	39
41			40
42			
43	140		
44			
45			
46	150		
47			
48			
49	160		
50			
51			
52	170		
53			

When I explain that one of the things I do is travel around the countryside measuring the heights and girths of trees, some people become as curious and puzzled as three-year-old children. 'Why?' 'Well, to find out how big they can get.' 'But why?' 'Well, it's very illuminating to find out how big different kinds of tree are likely to grow in different areas.' 'Yes, but *why?*'

One benefit is clear: you have an opportunity to protect a large or remarkable tree by alerting its owner to how rare or nationally exceptional it is. Nurseries, too, are always wanting to know the likely sizes when mature of the seedlings they stock. But a lot of this book is devoted to the portraits, measurements and histories of fewer than two thousand unusual or landmark trees, and another way of phrasing the question might be: 'How much can so few records tell us about the status of trees in general?' There are perhaps 25,000,000 trees in Sussex - the figure fluctuating by many millions each year as saplings germinate and die.

It seems fair to say that the lone tree in a field, or the bright gold tree in a garden, is generally the eye-catching feature in the landscape, and will mean more to us than the bulk of trees in woods and hedges. Trees, again, because of the long associations they build up with their environment, are often among the most 'individual' of organisms. Anyone can tell a fox from a badger, but recognising the individual fox or the individual badger is far harder. Many people, by contrast, will be able to recognise individual trees which they pass on their way to work, without necessarily being able to say what kind they are. A measurement of height and trunk diameter exists as a kind of distinctive 'signature' for a tree, and, once you learn to visualise them, these simple figures can convey a surprising amount of information about the tree's vigour, environment or outstandingness.

The size and, in particular, the height of trees also makes a tremendous impact on our experience of place. Landscapes with many trees over 30m tall - the western Rother valley around Midhurst, or Capability Brown's parkland at Ashburnham - evoke a sense of dignity or peacefulness, even of well-being, which is lacking when exposure or poor soils - as in the lower Adur valley or the Wealden slopes north from Herstmonceux - limit the trees' growth to 15 or 20m.

'Among the innumerable residences with which [Sussex, plus Surrey] are so thickly studded', Elwes and Henry wrote near the end of *The Trees of Great Britain and Ireland*, 'no part of England would better repay the researches of anyone interested in trees, and we have probably missed some of great rarity.'

In 1993, when my own interest in trees revived, this position had, if anything, only been accentuated by a century's enthusiastic arboriculture. The indefatigable rovings of Alan Mitchell, along with the Sussex-based Vicky

All the measurements in this book take the following form:

height of tree (in metres) x diameter of the trunk (in centimetres) + diameters of any secondary trunks (if appropriate), measured @ 1.5m from the ground unless stated, in (year). If the year is omitted, the height, or the diameter, or both, have been estimated rather than measured, in recent years and with fair accuracy.

Tree heights are normally recorded with the aid of a hypsometer. A fixed-unit baseline is taped or paced, and the bottom and top of the tree sighted against a pendulum scale, which is calibrated to convert angle into units of height. In all but experienced hands, a hypsometer tends to be a dangerous weapon, lending an aura of accuracy to measurements inflated by sloping ground, a leaning tree, or high branches arching out towards the observer. On the few occasions when trees have been measured by someone climbing them with a tape, heights estimated by hypsometer are sometimes found to be highly exaggerated.

Trunk diameters are measured by stretching a tape around the circumference, and discrepancies only arise when burrs, sprouts, buttresses or low branches have to be accommodated. The diameter must be taken at the narrowest point, if this is below 1.5m, and is otherwise measured at 1.5m unless the taper above this point is very abrupt. The tree's spread is seldom worth recording as it is directly dependent on other trees around.

Schilling, his co-founder of TROBI, had taken them to all of the county's 'famous' gardens, but many of the losses in the storms of 1987 and 1990 had still to be assessed. In Brighton, Peter Bourne had developed a passion for one threatened and understudied group, the elms, identifying and measuring many hundreds of examples in the South Downs Dutch Elm Disease control zones. But much remained to be discovered.

To locate and record a region's finest trees does require a rather bizarre hand of talents. The perfect dendrologist needs to be a walking encyclopaedia of the thousands of trees which can crop up anytime, anywhere: sometimes a mere glimpse of unusual foliage has to inform a decision to knock on the owner's door. He or she also needs to be a tireless diplomat, liaising with estate agents to obtain permission to visit sites, researching ownership, and cold-calling Jehovah's Witness fashion. (The good and the great of Sussex have proved wonderfully hospitable and welcoming; it is unusual to be summarily sent packing, and I have only had a guard-dog set loose on me once.) It is necessary, again, to be something of an athlete when the outstanding tree stands on a precipitous lake-bank or in a tangle of rhododendron branches: sometimes, confronted by an acre of brambles, measurers have been known to quail.

Most of the trees in this book were identified and measured by myself during several thousands of miles of foot travel - armed with binoculars (for spotting distant tell-tale foliage types), OS maps, TROBI identification badge, notebook and measuring gear. It is only at walking pace that trees off the beaten track are likely to be spotted; the county is fortunate in its vast network of public footpaths, which in the West are invariable walkable. Trains and buses are also just about frequent enough to transport you all around the county. It is only up the middle of the county, between Brighton and Crawley, that the volume of traffic on every road makes wayfaring unpleasant, and here most of the trees have been visited in the company of friends with cars, notably Philip Clarkson Webb, TROBI recorder for Kent.

For nearly all the records of elms (plus various other trees) I am indebted to Peter Bourne. Many other enthusiasts have also contributed information and the odd measurement, especially Nigel Muir in Chichester, Peter Davys (retired Dutch Elm Disease control officer for the Polegate area), Paul Strike (Milland tree warden), Frank Penfold (Sussex Wildlife Trust) and Tony Denyer (Chief Forestry Officer with East Sussex County Council for many years). Travel costs have been funded by the Sussex branch of the National Council for the Conservation of Plants and Gardens (NCCPG), and I am also indebted to Vicky Schilling and David Alderman at TROBI for furnishing me with historic information.

This book is neither accurate nor comprehensive. Birdwatching is easy, in that some basic assumptions can be made about what will and will not be seen.

United we stand. Perhaps the most curious trees in Sussex are these 'Siamese twin' ashes at Ashburnham Place, which fuse to make a single crown.

The scope of this book

7

Treewatching can only be undertaken with a mind open to finding anything, anywhere: thousands of species are grown in Britain, and there are trees at Borde Hill or Wakehurst Place which no-one has ever been able to identify with confidence. Furthermore, many of these species hybridise shamelessly, or have thrown up variously distinct forms which nurseries have independently named and propagated. The only comfort is that, once found, a tree stays put so that others can visit and check it for you. I have discreetly omitted to mention a few unsolved puzzles at a variety of sites, but the text is inevitably peppered with question marks.

My travels have carried me to, I would guess, nine out of ten of the county's finest trees. In well-known gardens, only the odd tree in a dark corner is likely to have been missed. Churchyards and town parks have all been visited, but a few private collections, and many odd trees in small gardens, have probably been unjustly overlooked. The worst omissions will doubtless be among native trees: I have tried to go to those places where experience suggests that these grow best, but, with 25 million to choose between, the search could go on forever.

Trees are continually being planted, growing, and dying. At best, this book is a cameo of the trees around the turn of the millennium: I have resisted the temptation to mention too many past 'champions'. And if, after twenty years, it has been superseded because of new trees which people have been inspired to plant, or to discover, then it will have done its job.

The landscape of coastal exposure: wind-sculpted hawthorn near Beachy Head.

Trees in the Landscape

*E*ven more than most English counties, Sussex contains an extraordinary variety of landscapes within its 400 square kilometres. In this variety, the relative abundance and size of the trees, and the different kinds that will grow, have a huge part to play.

Several elements combine to form these fluctuating patterns of tree-growth around the county, the most important of which, not surprisingly, is the human land-use, and indeed the history of land-use, sometimes extending back over thousands of years. Trees growing on land which has been wooded for centuries generally do much better than those planted in fields or new gardens. (One factor affecting the health of a tree which we still do not properly understand is the association formed between the feeding roots and the filaments, or mycorrhiza, of fungus species which are present in great variety in woodland soils but often absent from grassland or wasteland.) A young tree also benefits from the shelter of bigger trees on either side. Trees such as oaks and beeches, with big seeds, tend not to migrate far from one generation and the next, and so local population characteristics can accrue: if trees with long, straight boles are planted or selected, their offspring may dominate a wood centuries later.

Influence of human land-use

The other variables which affect the growth and distribution of trees, in descending order of significance, are the soil, the proximity of the sea, the local climate, and levels of pollution.

The county's varied geology makes for many different soil types, and no trees grow wild on all of them. The chalk is alkaline and rain drains straight through it; sandstones lack various trace elements; clay is impermeable and often waterlogged. Oaks and rowans die on an alkaline soil, because their roots cannot obtain enough iron. Ashes and maples struggle in sand, because too few nutrients are available. Beech and whitebeam thrive on chalk or sand, but hate a waterlogged soil. Alder and willow, by contrast, need it wet. A skilled eye soon picks up a subterranean change from gault clay to Folkestone beds, or from Wadhurst clay to Ashdown sand, simply by the change in vegetation. Soil preferences tend to be even more marked among planted trees, whose requirements are often imperfectly matched by the local environment anyway.

Geology and soil

In the Hastings Country Park are two valleys, Ecclesbourne Glen and Fairlight Glen. Both are full of ferns and mosses and have perhaps always been wooded, both are ringed with sandstone outcrops and slope precipitously down to the sea. But there is one overwhelming difference between the valleys, which creates a quite different sense of place. In Fairlight Glen, the oaks and ashes tower to 30m. In Ecclesbourne Glen, you can reach up and touch the canopy, and the trees struggle to exceed 5m.

Sea-winds and salt

The difference hinges on the aspect of the two valleys. Fairlight Glen faces just east of south, so that the sea-winds, which are always strongest from the south-west, are deflected by the right-hand lip of the glen. Ecclesbourne Glen is angled more to the west, and the gales are funnelled straight up it.

No part of Sussex is more than 40km from the sea, and the coastline itself is over 150km long. Sea-winds are salt-laden, and salt is toxic to most plants, as can be seen in the case of trees growing in the run-off zones from regularly-gritted roads; after the gale of January 1990, hollies far inland shed all their leaves. Curiously, perhaps, we have no native trees which, like mangroves, love to be beside the sea-side (though tamarisk and sea buckthorn are near-native shrubs with some special adaptations).

On the Downs, on the ridges above Hastings, or on the levels near the sea, the trees all lean from the south-west, their branches streaming like blown hair. Woodland trees huddle together, their tops clipped like topiary, and whole treescapes seem slanted slightly, like the pile of a carpet. This is not because the trees have been permanently bent into these positions by the force of the wind. During summer, they sprout in all directions but the tender shoots on the wind-ward side get killed off by the first salty gales of autumn, leaving only the branches on the downwind edge to grow on in the trees' own shelter. This wind-sculpture is particularly marked in yew trees, which are in leaf during the worst of the gales and grow slowly over a very long period of time: even the three ancient yews in the sheltered valley at Crowhurst cower from the distant and invisible sea, like vegetable monuments to endurance.

There are very few places in Sussex where anything like natural woodland still runs down to the shingle - parts of Chichester Harbour, around Atherington, and in the Hastings Country Park. The artificiality of the coastal scene is accentuated by the often more conspicuous growth of non-native trees - the belts of Monterey pine on the Ham Manor estate at Angmering, the Monterey cypresses of suburban Seaford, the ancient holm oaks of Southwick, the lines of hybrid poplar on Selsey Bill. Among native trees perhaps only elms were able to make big, shapely specimens in extreme exposure, and the elm as a mature tree is now restricted to a few patches on the eastern Downs.

Climate

The variations in weather records between one part of the county and the next hardly sound significant. Rainfall depends largely on altitude - the hills are often swathed in drizzly clouds and tend to attract thunderstorms - and there is a slight decrease from west to east as rain-fronts exhaust themselves on their

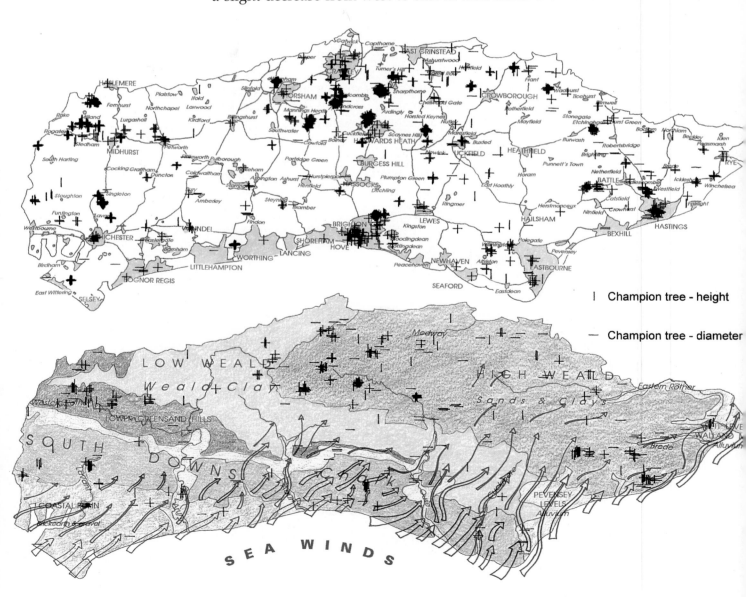

| Champion tree - height

— Champion tree - diameter

journey from the Atlantic. The Downs above Chichester receive over 1000mm a year, whilst Pevensey Levels and Rye Harbour get by on 650 - 700mm. Air frosts are half as frequent and much less severe along the coasts than they are inland, but differences almost as great occur between slopes sheltered by trees and 'frost pockets' open to the sky. Continental air cold enough to kill tender plants is slightly more likely to sweep into the east of the county than the west. On a summer afternoon, the coasts tend to be perhaps 3^0C cooler than inland areas, and the top of a 250m hill is 3^0 cooler than a lowland valley. Clouds tend to built up inland when sea-breezes keep coastal skies clear: Eastbourne and Selsey enjoy 1800 hours of sunshine a year, while inland in the east the total is about 1550 hours.

For our native trees, which are all adapted to these general climatic parameters, these minor variations have no perceptible effect. (Some, notably small-leaved lime and wild service, are at the edge of their range here in that summers are hardly ever warm enough for fertile seeds to be produced, but their distribution is the result of a slightly warmer spell 6000 years ago: there is no obvious correlation between their abundance and the hotter, inland areas.) Many cultivated trees, however, come from climates which are very much warmer, wetter or milder than ours, so that the small fluctuations between one end of Sussex and the other can mean the difference between a happy life and a slow, miserable death.

The New Zealand cabbage tree (*Cordyline australis*) is a popular plant in gardens all along the coast, but 7^0 of frost will kill it, so it is scarce and short-

The upper map (*facing page*) plots all the 'champion trees' of Sussex: the tallest and the stoutest recorded specimens. The lower map plots only the champions of those trees which are widespread or common.

Since 19 out of 20 of the kinds of tree in Sussex are neither native nor naturalised, the trees in the upper map inevitably cluster around centres of population (or those areas where the small percentage of the population with an interest in cultivating trees traditionally chose to live). The remarkable concentration of historic 'wild gardens' in the western High Weald - between Warnham, East Grinstead and Haywards Heath - shows up clearly, though it could just as well be argued that the Edwardian plantsmen settled in this part of the county because they knew it grew trees particularly well. Most older towns - Chichester, Midhurst, Arundel, Brighton, Lewes, Eastbourne, Hastings and Rye - boast clusters of champions; Crawley and Haywards Heath only fail to show up because they merge into a countryside full of notable trees. The build-up of nutrients within an ancient settlement, and the constant shelter offered by tall buildings, probably contribute to these clusters (even though many conifers do not thrive in polluted, town air). The prominence in the upper map of Brighton (and to a lesser degree of Eastbourne and Alfriston) is due to these towns' location within the South Downs Dutch Elm Disease (DED) control zones: none of the champion elms here are now widespread trees, and the pattern disappears on the lower map.

'Famous' tree collections such as Wakehurst Place and Borde Hill are still conspicuous in the lower map, even though the rare species for which these collections are renowned are not shown in it. This continued emphasis is partly an artefact of the survey method: such sites were at least taped for their everyday trees whereas many 'ordinary' small woods and farms have not been.

However, garden trees which later become widespread tend to be grown experimentally in the large collections first, so they have a head start here. Old parks such as Sheffield, Cowdray or Petworth also inherit good, woodland soils containing plenty of the fungi with which many trees benefit through making mycorrhizal associations, while their existing trees shelter and promote the growth of all new plantings. The final factor is the 'survival of the least fit' in the countryside at large, where the most vigorous trees have traditionally been cropped for timber in their reproductive youth, leaving their runtish peers to parent the next generation. This tends not to have pertained in gentlemen's parks, and some locally distinct populations of wild trees of good growth seem to have developed here.

The lower map shows how some Sussex soils are much likelier than others to produce a champion tree. The coastal plain around Chichester is fertile, but the exposure here tends to rule out champions for height. Chalk soils are also good for tree-growth, but the downland champions - including many of the county's tallest trees - are all concentrated in the shelter of the river-valleys, coombs and scarps. West of Pulborough, the greensand hills contain a remarkable concentration of champions, but the sticky clay plain of the Low Weald (and the eastern Levels) have hardly any. The largest numbers of champions are in the High Weald, a hilly country of mixed sands and clays: they tend to be concentrated around the fringes of the zone, and near the sea at Hastings, where the hills are more broken and the shelter of the valleys is greatest, but this distribution partly reflects the lower population densities in the central eastern Weald. Northwards and eastwards from Hastings and Battle, the hills are lower and the increased exposure again means there are few champions for height.

This Sitka spruce by the lake at Claremont School near Hastings is the largest in eastern England - but could have reached such a size only in a rainy, sheltered valley near the sea.

lived inland. A London plane needs plenty of hot sunshine to ripen its wood: the refreshing sea-breezes of the Sussex coast have a stunting effect, and only in a few lowland areas in the interior do the trees begin to attain the stature of those in any London park. A Douglas fir, again, comes from the mountains of Oregon and British Columbia which are much wetter than Sussex. Planted high up in the Weald (and given enough side-shelter) it will make a giant of 40m. Planted at sea-level, it may struggle to reach 10m and die at 50. The needs of other species seem to be more complex: the phillyrea, a seldom-recognised Mediterranean evergreen, is hardy throughout Sussex, but the largest trees are near the sea and away from the east, suggesting a preference for mild winters and reasonably warm summers. Sitka spruce, another Rocky Mountain giant, typically grows in coastal groves; all the big boles in Sussex are where the rainy High Weald meets the sea, around Hastings.

Forms of environmental pollution which affect tree-growth in Sussex include salt run-off from gritted roads; sulphur dioxide, nitrogen dioxide, particulates and other effects of burning fossil fuels; and over-enrichment of the soil from agricultural fertilisers. The classic indicators of sulphur dioxide pollution are lichens; some Sussex sites (notably the old deer-parks of Parham, Eridge and Ashburnham) have exceptionally varied lichen populations, and the county-wide picture is that, away from the towns, the mean air quality is better than anywhere in central and eastern England, but not as good as in the far west. A hundred years ago

the air was cleaner, and several lichen species have been lost as a result. A number of conifers - especially silver firs and spruces - are also extremely sensitive to sulphur dioxide pollution, and to soot and smoke particles which clog their resinous foliage. In 1911, a Norway spruce was the tallest tree known in Sussex - and Britain as a whole - at 46m, but spruce growth is now restricted and trees of 30m survive only in a few favoured spots in West Sussex; younger specimens, in apparently suitable locations, now ail and die when they are much smaller.

'Ash dieback' is a mysterious disease currently affecting ashes in a fairly distinct area of the Low Weald, north of the Downs. The trees die back at no great age and may be killed completely. This is one of the most intensively-farmed parts of the county, and chemicals building up in the soil are probably a contributory factor; oaks and other trees growing in heavily-cropped fields may sometimes show comparable symptoms.

A journey around Sussex might begin in the coastal plain around Chichester - a horizontal landscape of expansive glasshouses, flooded gravel workings, weed-grown aerodromes and wide lanes stretching into the distance. It is pierced by the one great spire of Chichester cathedral, and a thousand smaller spires of poplar trees which, in the winds from the channel, grow taller than the native species. Trees are numerous, in farm shelterbelts and bungalow gardens, but the closely-set villages and the easily-tilled, gravelly soils have meant that there are no woods of size, and few at all, and hardly any wasted corners for native trees to colonise. The lack of woodland, and the stocky growth of what trees there are, make for a uniquely bright, open countryside, all silvery willows and sunshine and fresh, salt air: even the character of the people who live here seems to have become friendlier and at ease. It also makes for an egalitarian, unimposing landscape, a mishmash of small things - little inlets of sea, where wavelets lap against spinneys and hedges; small-holdings, market gardens and little family nurseries specialising in bedding plants, wall to wall through Earnley; a thousand low-roofed cottages but no big, stately homes.

The Chichester coastal plain

The coastal plain around Chichester: 'a horizonatal landscape of expansive glasshouses, flooded gravel workings, weed-grown aerodromes and wide lanes stretching into the distance.'

Chichester itself has settled into that happy mix of trees and buildings of most old cities, with plump, sedate lime and horse chestnut crowns mellowing the rooftops. One of the most extraordinary sights, however, in a county full of extraordinary trees, is in The Broadway - a somewhat bijou street - where the noted dendrologist Nigel Muir has a pocket-handkerchief garden scarcely 4m wide. The front is an exuberant jungle of strange, evergreen leaves; there are three trees too rare and tender to feature in this book (*Quercus salicina*, *Cornus capitata*, and the lovely *Eriobotrya deflexa*). The back is divided into the Chinese Arboretum (left hand side) and the Japanese Arboretum (on the right). The neighbours' reactions are mixed.

As you go eastwards, the coastal plain dwindles into an increasingly windswept and urbanised apron beneath the Downs. Only tiny windows of open country remain along the 45km of coast between Aldwick and Brighton: a few fields, scrubby woods and lanes which led once to the drowned village of Atherington and now end together and unexpectedly at a deserted shingle beach; or near the mouth of the Adur, where the A27 flyover, the river's tidal breadth, and the chapel of Lancing College make up one of the few memorable Sussex views where the impact of trees lies in their absence.

It is sad but perhaps inevitable that all the places in Sussex where more or bigger trees would be most welcome are those where trees, because of the salty winds, are least inclined to grow. Felpham, Middleton, East Preston, Lancing, Kingston - the distinct old villages have all been swallowed up by the angular grey teeth of 1950s and 60s bungaloid sprawl, and, to anyone looking for interesting trees, the windswept playing fields of Goring are uniformly boring and the streets of Bognor Regis all very tedious.

On a summer's afternoon, the little powderpuff clouds that appear over Selsey Bill or Littlehampton become the white flocks of the plain, and finally rear up into stately cumulus above the Downs. The natural rhythm is the same as the stunted trees of the coast imperceptibly grow taller and eventually develop into the monumental cedars of Goodwood or the beeches around Slindon. The terrain, too, like a gigantic, petrified wave, swells up from the plain and finally breaks above the county's interior.

The Sussex Downs really comprise two very different landscapes, between which you can draw a line with some precision along the tranquil valley of the Arun. The distinction is owed in part to medieval history, and in part to the influence of the sea. Westwards from the river Arun, the whole of the Downs were once engrossed in the hunting forests of Arundel and Stansted; woodlands were preserved, and only the smallest hamlets grew up. Eastwards, the state-of-the-art agriculture of prehistoric times continued its unbroken development, and many villages developed in the shelter of the deans and coombs. Here, the sea-winds sweep straight in over the rooftops of Worthing or Hove;

The western Sussex Downs: 'a country of stretching forests and giant trees.'

westwards, they have the Isle of Wight and the breadth of the Chichester plain to cross first, and shed their load of salt spray *en route*.

These elements have combined to create, in the west, a country of stretching forests and giant trees, and, in the east, of bare ploughland and a few, huddling copses. The depopulated landscape of the western Downs has an

Broad-leaved limes: 'Towering, aristocratic, iron-grey stems.'

almost continental flavour, with its straight forest roads and rides, its far-flung great mansions - Stansted and Uppark - in their wide parks, and its mile upon mile of young beech plantation, which are some of the few places in southern England where you can still stand and listen to the silence. The highest part of the Sussex Downs is here, at Tegleaze - an oakwood with bluebells. On the continuously-wooded scarps, the native tree communities of the chalk survive intact, and, for anyone who has grown up among the birches, rowans or alders of the Weald, these hanging forests are almost as eerily different as a jungle. Box-trees appear in place of holly; junipers invest the sheep-walks with their fairy-tale turrets, and subterranean yew-groves cloak the slopes; the occasional whitebeam lights up a dark coomb. If you are lucky, you will stumble upon a stand of the wild broad-leaved lime, with their towering, aristocratic, iron-grey stems.

River-gaps and dry valleys dissect the Downs in the east into a series of memorable land-forms - the Seven Sisters; the isolated cone of Mount Caburn; Firle Beacon's snub-nosed summit - like a trail of Henry Moore sculptures. Few trees clutter this architecture: sometimes the ungrazed turf has been choked with thorn and ash, as in the lower depths of the Devil's Dyke or the scarps above Eastbourne. High on the Stanmer estate behind Brighton, storm-blasted beech hangers - those characteristic nineteenth-century adornments of open downs - stand like ruined temples. The catchment area of Eastbourne's water-supply has been safeguarded by the single large beech plantation of Friston Forest.

These eastern Downs are also one of the world's dwindling landscapes with elms. These noble trees play their most conspicuous role in the valley of the Cuckmere - the narrowest and most sheltered of the river-gaps, and a landscape so perfect that sometimes every adventitious thorn-bush looks as if it has obtained planning permission to grow there. Elsewhere - under the brunt of onshore winds and the constant depletions of DED, and hidden from twentieth-century developments and choc-a-block dual carriageways and vast, pesticide-drenched ploughlands - the ancient landscape of elm trees survives only around such tiny oases of calm as Bishopstone, Folkington and the East Sussex West Dean.

There is a painful contrast between ancient and modern downland settlements. Alfriston and Regency Brighton nestle in deep valleys where trees grow tall between the buildings. Arundel and Lewes spill over low, riverbank hills around their castles, but higher ground on either hand still offers shelter, and both towns can boast some very fine trees. Seaford, Hove, Newhaven, and above all Peacehaven, by contrast, brave out the worst of the sea gales, and only a few cypresses and pines are able to mitigate many of their bleak townscapes. Brighton is very densely built, so its innumerable street trees - elms, with some sycamores - have a vital role to play. The town inherits a tradition of enthusiastic arboriculture, with many new disease-resistant elms getting their first field trials in the suburbs.

The Downs are not the highest hills in Sussex. This accolade goes to Black Down, which spectacularly announces the arrival of the lower greensand hills from Surrey. The name is evocative: a silent forest of dark Scots pine broods on the hill's broad, flat summit and cloaks the steep flanks; the soil is a dark, sour sand; thunderstorms frequently mass overhead. The contrast with the white, sunny, windswept Downs could hardly be greater.

The geology of the region needs to be explained here. The chalk forms the uppermost layer in a sequence of sediments laid down when Sussex was a shallow sea or swamp. The sediments became a mountain, and the mountain had its summit worn away like an opened, soft-boiled egg: the chalk is the egg-shell, still projecting at the rim. Underneath the chalk is a narrow band of upper greensand, which looks a lot like chalk. Underneath this comes a sticky, oozing bed of gault clay - neither are thick enough to form significant landscape features. Next is the lower greensand: on top the Folkestone beds which make the barren, silver-sand heaths of Stedham and West Chiltington Commons; then the soft, fertile Sandgate beds of the western Rother (characteristically green when first exposed, but quickly oxidising to a fierce, Sahara red); then underneath them the hard, poor Hythe beds of Black Down itself. Under the steep scarps of these greensand hills, the Atherfield and Weald clays form a broad lowland - the yolk of the egg.

The sequence of hills to the south of the Weald clay is mirrored by the sequence to the north, ending in the North Downs. The westernmost stretch of the clay (the Milland Vale) is only 2km wide, so that Black Down (part of the northern hills) stands face to face with the hills on the southern side which form Bexleyhill and Woolbeding Commons.

The greensand soils are not noted as good farmland, but one peculiarity has long been remarked: many kinds of trees grow taller and faster here than perhaps anywhere else in the country. Arguably the biggest trunk in Britain, that of the Queen Elizabeth Oak in Cowdray Park, stands only 500m from the site, in 1911, of Britain's tallest tree; 500m in the other direction, the most massive chestnut currently known is growing vigorously.

Dramatic and almost mountainous though the ramparts of the Milland Vale are, all glimpses of them in summertime are practically lost under dank, rampant verdure: this is an intimate, secret landscape, full of deep hollow ways, unexpected mansions and quirky re-entrants. Along the scarps, chestnut coppices run for miles, many cut on a short rotation for the walking-stick industry (the factory used to operate in the Vale; now - such is progress - the poles are exported to Germany and the finished sticks brought back again); further east is the great wooded common of the Mens. On the gently-shelving heights, pinewoods and clearings of improved farmland continually replace one another; in the valleys which pierce the ridges, for instance above Chithurst and Lodsworth, great sessile oaks and beeches tower. Stone cottages and fine old houses seem dwarfed by the trees which loom above them on all sides, and which would strike terror into most householders of the lowlands. Millionaires with a fondness for privacy are attracted here, and iron gates and security signs do nothing to further the country's welcome to strangers.

Between the rising ground of the Hythe beds and the wall of the Downs, the western Rother winds through the greensand and is the nearest thing Sussex can boast to a proper, grown-up river, with rocky lengths and clear, weed-grown pools, steep wooded banks and otters. Its vale is an expansive, expensive land of great houses and great, well-spaced trees; the old parks of Cowdray and Petworth are here (with Parham just beyond the Rother's confluence with the Arun), and, apart from the pinewoods around Ambersham, almost all the valley resembles one tremendous parkland.

East of the Arun, the greensand quickly dwindles - first to the small-scale, pretty landscape of paddocks, knolls and commonland cottages between

Pulborough and Storrington, then to a narrow bank of undulating country distinguished, if at all, by the superior growth of the oaks and poplars which crown it. Henfield and Hurstpierpoint are perched upon this ridge.

Seen from the tops of the greensand or the Downs, the plain of the Low Weald in the centre of Sussex looks a little like a giant maze. Fields, hamlets and small towns are all fringed by shaws and small woods of the never-tall, dark-leaved trees of the clay - field maple, hornbeam, Midland thorn, wild service and, above all, oak - which, with distance, seem to blend into one primeval forest. And to enter this landscape is also like entering a maze: except for glimpses of the frowning wall of the Downs, the prospects tend to be limited by the low terrain to a few hundred metres; and the same motifs - spreading oak tree, narrow lane with fast cars, race-horse in paddock, half-timbered manor, business park - repeat themselves again and again, from Fernhurst as far east as the Ouse and from Rusper south to Small Dole.

The heavy, often waterlogged soils make good farmland, but very seldom produce monumental, landmark trees; few keen gardeners have braved them, and giants such as the wellingtonia - leading citizens in the tree-communities of the High Weald - only sicken and sulk here. The fine cedar avenue and the trees in the Pleasure Grounds at Knepp Castle, at the very heart of this land-scape, are an exception to prove the rule. In the far north, under the flight-path from Gatwick, a few beds of harder rock - Horsham Stone and 'Sussex Marble' - create a more undulating landscape with conspicuously more upwardly-mobile trees; the famous gardens of Warnham Court are located on one of these ridges. Towns on the plain - Burgess Hill, Hassocks, Hailsham - are largely modern, and their environment still suffers from a lack of bigger, mature trees.

Many trees grow best on lower greensand soils. The yew at Coldwaltham Church is the largest and oldest in Sussex.

East of the river Ouse, the Low Weald is swept by seawinds channelled through the river-gaps in the Downs. Trees are far fewer, ragged hedges replacing the shaws of oak. Railway poplars - all tilted the same way so that the whole landscape seems slightly on edge - become the most conspicuous tree, except when the blackthorn blooms. Finally the landscape settles into the willowy expanse of the Pevensey Levels, fronting the sea. South of the Levels sprawls Eastbourne - its newer developments almost treeless, its fine Victorian streets graced with elms and pines, huddling in the shelter of the Downs.

The hills, often cloud-capped and pierced by tall conifers, which are the northern skyline of most views from the Downs, form the High Weald. This is where the rocks underlying all the other Wealden layers are exposed at the surface, their clays and hard sands mashed together by millions of years of faulting and mountain-building. It is a varied and sometimes little-known landscape, full of surprises. The Victorian *nouveaux riches* loved it, and built their mock castellations and icing-sugar palazzi here to face the distant Downs or the sea, and planted their cedars, cypresses and redwoods, which for the most part loved it too. Three out of four champion trees of Sussex today are growing in the High Weald.

The boundaries of the region are not distinct - at Horsham, its westward limits are best indicated by the sudden soil-change to the poor and often uncultivated sands of St Leonards Forest. Across the birch-grown heaths and pine plantations the land rises steadily. As you travel south on the A23, the trees around disguise the sense of height, but the rather tattered wellingtonias which line the Handcross Park side of the road march along the horizon in any view from the western Low Weald. The flat plain to the north around Gatwick, however, is considerably higher than the upper Ouse valley to the south, so that, beyond Handcross, the terrain falls away suddenly and unexpectedly.

You could almost imagine that some heavenly gardener had scattered a huge packet of tree seeds over the Ouse headwaters. Here, almost within sight

The clays of the Sussex Low Weald encourage plentiful oaks, field maples, hornbeams, Midland thorns and wild service trees.

of each other's trees, are the famous old gardens of Borde Hill, Wakehurst Place, Leonardslee, Nymans, South Lodge, the High Beeches and Sheffield Park. The gaps in between are filled with steep fields, tall woods of oak and ash, and pine and Douglas fir plantations.

The towns in this part of Sussex (Crawley, Horsham, Haywards Heath, East Grinstead and Uckfield) are largely the products of recent prosperity, but all have plenty of trees - in old parks like Horsham Park, in streets and surrounding woods, and growing happily in gardens everywhere. In Crawley, the big field and shaw oaks were retained when the new town was developed, and many streets are triumphs of imaginative 1950s planting. I once spent the whole of a spring day happily tramping the town, recording the many different cherries and crabs in bloom.

One of the many great gardens of the western High Weald, Sheffield Park is famous for the vivid autumn colours reflected in its lakes.

At the heart of the High Weald is Ashdown Forest, where the sandy ridges gather together into a wider upland of heather, gorse and bracken. Clumps of pine (replacing round groves of holly) were first planted on the hilltops in the eighteenth century to guide wayfarers, and they have since spread widely across the ungrazed heath. The moorland is intersected by the garish green of fertilised fields, by modern pine planta-tions and ancient beechwoods - containing huge pollards - and by a few Victorian parks. At its northern edge the river Medway starts its journey to the Thames estuary, flowing through a well-tended countryside notable for tall wellingtonias. Crowborough, to the east, perches precariously on the highest of the Wealden hills - a compara-tively windswept settlement with huge skies, but the bigger gardens in the ghylls all around are crammed with ornamental conifers.

A High Weald scene: aspens at Mayfield.

In the northern corner of East Sussex, between Crowborough and Wadhurst, is a region of steep hills - pyramidal Saxonbury Hill with its iron-age hill-fort and crest of beeches, Mayfield Hill crowded by its church spire and mellow roofs, Argos Hill with its windmill - and deep dark ghylls where rocky streams tumble: one of the finest and least-known of Sussex landscapes, full of steep, winding lanes, tall dignified trees, and dead-end hollow-ways. Red-tiled farmsteads are scattered like little boats riding a mountainous sea, and many mansions of the fashionable hinterland of Tunbridge Wells are almost hidden among the trees and ridges. The medieval Forest of Waterdown partly survives in the beechwoods and open plains of Eridge Park.

The long ridge from Uckfield to Burwash and Battle, and the valleys of the upper Rother and the Dudwell, are less steep and intricate, and offer less shelter from the sea in the south. This part of the county remains profoundly rural, the only town being the largely modern Heathfield, and there are few grand houses. The main ridge - site of the medieval Dallington Forest - is now the most extensively coniferised landscape in Sussex, with many gloomy

Ashdown Forest.

hemlock and Norway spruce plantations. The long southern flanks of the ridge, as they subside into the Low Weald, form a quiet, meagre countryside of wind-clipped woods, tiny fields and little, muddy farms which were never prosperous. Even the place-names hereabouts seem to have a doleful sound to them: Muddles Green; Foul Mile; Terrible Down; World's End Farm.

The southernmost of the Wealden ridges runs from Ashburnham, through Battle, to confront the Channel in the high cliffs around Hastings. The presence of shelter becomes increasingly important for tree-growth: the magnificent wooded estates of Ashburnham Place and Beauport Park are on the inland side of the ridge, and help to define its exceptionally well-treed character; Normanhurst, another big Victorian park, is high on the crest and its conifers are landmarks from the Pevensey Levels. These hills are more often swathed in low cloud than the inland ridges, which has undoubtedly helped the Normanhurst trees to reach such a size.

Hastings, like Brighton, has grown up from a fishing town to spread over a series of deeply-cut valleys. Alexandra Park, St Leonards Gardens, Linton Gardens and St Helens Woods all nestle within these steep coombs and contain exceptionally fine trees for a coastal situation; the urban ridges are rather bleak and often the only street trees are very young ones. Bexhill (like Hove) lies beyond the sheltering hills and few native trees poke their heads over the rooftops.

The eastern corner of the High Weald, cut off from the rest of the county by the Hastings ridge, is a very distinct region, neat and somehow geometrical. The many hills all conform to a maximum height of 100 metres; they are separated by tentacles of sheep-grazed marshland which extend from the broad vale of the lower Eastern Rother and the Pett and Walland levels. White weatherboarding becomes the architectural norm; oast-houses and apple orchards abound, sheltered by neatly-clipped belts of grey alder; there are hop-gardens with their tall grids of chestnut poles; the Lombardy poplar replaces the wellingtonia as the king-pin of the landscape. Woodlands are abundant, especially around Beckley where wild boar, escaped from specialist pig-farms, have been living wild for several years. Some are coniferised, but there is still an unusual proportion of working coppices.

Uniquely in Sussex, the hilltop houses of Rye and Winchelsea look out to sea from the shelter of fine trees: the prevailing south-westerly winds, blowing across the ridge from Hastings, no longer carry enough salt to seriously impair tree-growth, and it is the north-easterlies out of Kent which the birdwatcher at Rye Harbour fears most. Even the levels, underneath the old towns, have many willow trees amid their prefabricated bungalows, while the view eastwards into Romney Marsh is thronged with lines of poplars. The eastern fringes of the county, in fact, closely mirror the western plain where we began.

Great trees of the eastern High Weald include the wild service with the biggest recorded bole, at Parsonage Farm, Udimore.

The deer park at Eridge has a recorded history stretching back to the Norman conquest. Trees such as this beech - the largest in Britain - have been pollarded for centuries to provide fodder for deer.

Trees in History

The Wildwood

Five hundred human generations ago (and perhaps fifty oak generations), in the wake of the last ice age, the first birch and willow trees recolonised Sussex, which was then a highland massif in the heart of a continent. Rapidly, the climate warmed: hazel, scots pine, oak and ash, and finally beech, hornbeam and lime, crowded into the country, while rising seas lapped around the hills and finally cut off the access for further species. For thousands of years, wild bison, giant cattle called aurochs, beavers, bears and boars, along with hunting and gathering tribes, frequented a forest - the Wildwood - which was broken only by cliff-top meadows, storm-blown glades, and valley swamps. The stumps and fallen logs of this forest can still be seen, pickled in seawater and cushioned by sand, during low tides off Bexhill and Pett Level; but these trees were only the last guard of windswept survivors, retreating as the tide overwhelmed them. At Filsham reedbeds, St Leonards, 8000-year-old hazel nuts can be picked out of the peat whenever dykes are dug or deepened.

Fairlight Glen: the Wildwood.

But the aurochs, and the giant trees under which they browsed, are gone beyond recreation. A canoe excavatated in East Anglia had been dug out of a single unbranched oak-log 18m long and 2m thick, and no trees approaching this stature are left in Britain now. You might imagine, then, that nothing like the scene of the county's first colonisation by trees, or like the Wildwood in its prime, could be found in Sussex today.

Fortunately, they can be - within 500m of each other, in the Hastings Country Park. Sometime between 300 and 500 years ago, a gigantic landslip here created Covehurst Wood, a platform of boulders and fresh-water pools underneath the high cliff, fronting the waves of the Channel. Ferns, lichens and mosses (one found on Scilly but nowhere else in the northern hemisphere) have crusted the boulders, and in the soil which has accumulated between them a bonzai forest has grown, consisting of thorns, sallows, hazels, wizened oaks and elms scarcely taller than a person. There is a strange, sweet-and-sour sense of a landscape at once primeval, and very young.

The sides of Fairlight Glen, which tumbles down to the sea a stone's throw away, are precipitous - too steep and too wet for much timber extraction ever to have been feasible. Here, surely, is a tiny pocket of 'primary' woodland: at no stage since the ice age has the natural tree-cover been cleared away. The trees crowd together - the bole of a sessile oak below the Dripping Well runs straight for 25m - leaning into one another and lying, everywhere, as they have fallen, to become gardens of multicoloured toadstools and insect goldmines. (A quarter of the British fauna depends directly or indirectly on decaying timber at some stage in its life-cycle.) One huge ash stood for three winters where it had died in 1995: that autumn, it bristled with yellow honey-fungus, shining like light-bulbs up the bole. The air here is cool in a heatwave and humid in the depths of a drought; rare mosses and liverworts thrive in the spray of the cascading stream just as they did seven thousand years ago. Such moist, continuously-wooded High Wealden ghylls are renowned for harbouring outlying populations of plants, like Cornish moneywort or Tonbridge filmy fern, which have otherwise retreated far into the rainy west of Britain.

The golden age of which Fairlight Glen is in some ways a relic came to an end in about 4000BC with two contemporaneous events. Firstly, the climate began to cool slightly again. Trees such as wild service and small-leaved lime - the commonest Wildwood tree - could no longer ripen their seeds: their populations became fossilised, reproducing themselves only from suckers and sprouts and dwindling slowly into rare trees of undisturbed woods and ancient hedgerows.

The first farmers

Simultaneously, the first farmers began to sail in from the continent. They settled on the Downs, as the soils were fertile and easily tilled at a time when most of the Weald was a quagmire. Using stone axes and fire, they began to carve their way through the great forests.

Coppicing

Except in the case of pine, felling a native tree seldom kills it. Instead, the tree's biological clock is re-set: shoots spring up from the stump, or 'stool', with all the vigour of saplings - a sallow 'coppiced' in this way can regrow four metres in three months. Continual browsing (and fire or grubbing) will eventually have killed off the stools in the new fields, but the coppice growth would, in the meantime, have supplied the new agriculturalists with all the small-sized poles they needed for fencing, barns, huts and firewood. A neolithic log track over the marshes - like the Sweet Track in Somerset - was uncovered in 1997 during the development of the Hampden Park area of Eastbourne.

Ashcombe Bottom, 4km west of Lewes, is one of the very few ancient woodlands left on the East Sussex Downs. Even here, some soil profiles reveal the downhill creep and impoverishment connected with agricultural clearance some time in the past. However, the hazel coppice supports a colony of dormice - an exclusively arboreal rodent - to which for millennia this wood must have been a kind of ark in an ocean of open fields. Among the hazels

Ashcombe Bottom: a rare ancient woodland on the East Sussex Downs.

grow many spreading oaks, their branches festooned with polypody and hartstongue ferns. Oaks dislike chalk but thrive here because the acid clays deposited on top the chalk have not been dispersed by ploughing or erosion.

Near the top of the wood, maps mark an 'ash'. Ash trees, left to grow tall, to set seed and then to rot and topple over, seldom complete their second century. But this one was chosen in the Dark or Middle Ages to mark the parish boundary between East Chiltington and St John Without, and may be far older. Four separate trunks exist today, 3m apart and perhaps 150 years old, each of them identical twins. These are the surviving stems of an immemorial coppice whose stool has long since rotted away; they grow in an arc and it is tempting to extrapolate a complete circle of outwards growth perhaps 20m across. In Leith Copse, on the Downs near Petersfield, the boundary between Sussex and Hampshire was marked in Saxon times by a rare broad-leaved lime, which has since propagated itself into a grove of stately trees.

Coppice stools are vulnerable to browsing (this may have been the nemesis of the palatable lime). Whenever pressures on land-use meant that cropped trees had to share *lebensraum* with livestock, they were 'pollarded' instead. Pollarding a tree involves cutting it, not at ground level, but three metres up, so that the tender sprouts are out of animals' reach. Like coppicing, this practice greatly prolongs the tree's life. Since axing off branches from the top of a ladder is never something to undertake lightly, and since Sussex has never been desperately short of woods, pollards have probably always been few and far between here. They are now largely confined to a few historic deer-parks - notably Cowdray where a number of medieval sessile oak pollards survive around the golf course - and to Ashdown Forest, where the commoners' stock once roamed at large and where beeches were pollarded to provide either timber or browse. In woods, trees were often cut at an intermediate height ('stubs') to serve as living markers for the block of coppice ('cant' or 'coup') to be cropped each winter. Surviving stubs are generally oak or hornbeam.

By the Iron Age, most of England had begun to take on the intensively-farmed aspect of the present day. The poor, swampy soils of the Weald were one of the few places where the wilderness hung on. Stane Street to Chichester and the routes

This huge hornbeam stool at Brede is the product of centuries' cutting in a medieval hedge-line.

to the Roman industrial complex at Beauport Park still had to cross a great forest: Anderita, or Andredesweald to the South Saxons. This forest was only extensively cleared for agriculture in the high Middle Ages, when soaring populations pushed small-holders into ever more marginal terrains. There is still a whiff of the frontier town about the settlements - with their modern English names - which grew up along the Wealden ridgeways: Woods Corner, Punnetts Town, Turners Hill. It is often still possible to recognise fields as individual clearings, bounded not by planted hedges but by uncut strips of forest called 'shaws'; there is little in the Weald of that complex overlay of landscape relics - tumuli, lynchets, prehistoric tracks - which characterises the South Downs and, indeed, most of lowland Britain. If there was little impact on this countryside before the Middle Ages, there was little impact afterwards: until Regency times the roads leading into and out of it were so bad that even the

Place Names

At the scale of the Ordnance Survey 1:50,000 series, there are about 150 place names in Sussex which refer not just to woodland but to particular trees: the main concentration is in the High Weald. Some are romantic concoctions, but many stand to show how important trees have always been in Sussex people's lives.

The oak - abundant, impressive and characterful - is celebrated more than any other tree: spreading 'Broad Oaks' and tall 'Fair Oaks', 'Lone Oaks' and oaks in groups of three to twelve; 'Burnt Oaks' struck by lightning; 'Scrag Oaks' sprouting from the stump; 'Royal Oaks' commemorating Charles II's escape at Boscobel; 'Mile Oaks' at intervals along highways; and 'Watch Oaks' from which children kept a look-out for the approaching mail-coach. (The current Watch Oak at Battle is only a sapling, the previous tree having been removed to construct the mini-roundabout.) Leonard Blomfield suggested in 1885 that 'Firle' might have something to do with fir-trees; ironically, it actually means 'land covered with oaks'.

Only slightly less frequent named are beech (Buxted, Buckhurst) and ash (Ashurst, Downash, Nash). Many of the beech names probably date from the nineteenth century, when beech became a fashionable tree.

Memorably rare trees were clearly useful for place-naming. Yew is the next most mentioned tree (Ifield, Iford, Iden, Ewhurst etc). Box trees are featured in the Anglo-Saxon names for sites well outside their current distribution: you can still find wild box near Boxgrove and Bexleyhill, but not at Bexhill or Bixley Wood (south-east of Beckley). Wild apples must also have been memorable (Crabtree; Apuldram; Wilding Wood): before the Battle of Hastings, Harold is recorded to have camped under a 'hoar apple tree' ('hoar' here meant 'boundary-marker'). Similarly distinct were pears, (Prinsted, Perryfield, Parham), plums (Plumpton, Broomhill), black poplars (Popular Farm at Forest Row), limes (Lindfield, Lentridge, Limbourne Farm), and the wild service or checkers tree (Chequers Farm at Cross-in-Hand or the Chequers inns at Battle and at Rowhook: the berries were once brewed into an alcoholic beverage).

At least 28 different kinds of tree get a mention all told: elms (Elmgrove Farm, River Limden), birches (Barkham, Burchetts Wood), osiers (Withyham), sallows (Salehurst), hawthorns (Thorney Island, Copthorne, Sharpthorne), hollies (Hollingrove), hazels (Nutbourne, Nuthurst, Nutley, Cowdray), alders (Albourne), aspens (Apsley Farm), elders (Elsted), blackthorns or sloes (Slaugham), field maples, cherries and sweet chestnuts. Among the exotics come pines, firs, larches, cedars, walnuts and, bizarrely, Myrtle Grove Farm and The Olives. Axletree, near Peasmarsh, presumably commemorates a tree felled for a waggon axle (or a mill post?); Summertree Farm near Cowbeech recalls the pre-Christian custom of bringing a leafy branch or 'summer tree' into the house in May. Curiously, some distinctive trees, such as hornbeam and rowan, never seem to have been chosen.

gentry made the weekly expedition to church in waggons which only oxen could drag through the several feet of liquid mud. Much of the High Weald remains a kind of landscape museum, the pattern of farm tracks, lanes, hedges, coppices and yeomen's farms very much as it was six centuries ago.

Sussex (after Surrey) is still the most wooded of British counties, even though the eastern Downs and the coastal plain and levels are almost without tree-cover. Within the High Weald, the percentage of woodlands is as high as it is in Europe as a whole. We owe this rich inheritance partly to poor soils and inaccessibility, but also largely to a phenomenon which has often, ironically, taken the blame for destroying trees: the Wealden iron industry.

The Wealden iron industry

A Tudor blast furnace needed big seams of iron ore, fast-flowing streams to turn its waterwheels, and large woods to hand where charcoal could be produced. These factors combined in the ghylls of the High Weald, which for two centuries became the nation's industrial heartland. Every few kilometres,

Trees for Timber

To plant an exotic tree for timber (sweet chestnut excepted) is largely a twentieth-century idea. Many native timbers have particular qualities and special uses and were traditionally cropped as needed. Oak was the timber for building with: it is tough, rot-proof and, when grown in the shelter of a wood, comes in long, straight lengths. By the eighteenth century, the standard forestry practice in the Weald was 'coppice-with-standards'. Young oaks ('tellows') were 'promoted' - or by Victorian times planted - among the coppice stools, growing long boles in competition with the young growth before spreading their crowns above the coppice layer, and adding girth for perhaps 150 years until felling. Occasionally ash or other trees were similarly treated.

The abundance of oak in Sussex woodlands is partly an artefact of its historical popularity: English oak was generally chosen, though the two native species are almost indistinguishable as timber trees and Plashett Wood, a Site of Special Scientific Interest near Isfield, is a large mature plantation of sessile oaks. On very light soils, oaks thrive but their timber is nearly always worthless because of 'shake' - annular cracking caused by drought-stress. Natural oak-woods on poor sands, therefore, were often coppiced instead: the regrowth is slow and twisted in comparison with most trees', but the bark on stems about 20 years old is particularly rich in the tannins needed to tan leather. The best-preserved sessile oak coppice in the county is at High Woods north of Bexhill, a nature reserve managed by the High Woods Preservation Society. The trees are crusted in moss and lichens and have low, writhing stems, almost as if they thought they were growing high on a mountainside in Wales.

Ash timber rots before oak does but is uniquely shatter-proof, making it the best native timber for tool-handles and waggon shafts: it takes to coppicing very well and provides the finest of firewoods.

Beech - best for indoor uses - came into fashion as a timber-tree relatively late. The eighteenth century plantations on the Downs were as much for ornament as future use, but it is now the most popular forestry tree. It coppices badly, and a group of ancient, gnarled

coppice stools in High Woods is a remarkable sight. Elm - the other really big native tree - produces a timber which hardly burns and never splits: its many uses included coffins and wheel-hubs. Farmland elms and parkland beeches were also occasionally pollarded so that their palatable foliage could provide fodder for stock.

Sweet chestnut was never grown as a 'standard' because its timber always becomes 'shaky' with age, but its fast-growing coppice stems are straight, rot-proof and easily cleft. Coppice plantations are abundant in the Weald and are often still worked, because of the market for chestnut palings and for the traditional Sussex cleft-rail fencing. However, because chestnut is not native and its heavy leaf-fall tends to suffocate woodland wildflowers, a pure coppice is of no more interest to wildlife than a spruce plantation.

Hazel used also to be widely planted for coppicing: it nearly always takes the form of a multi-stemmed bush, so it is hard to tell whether or not plants have recently been cropped. The straight young stems are so pliable that a strong wrist can twist them into a rope, and they remain in demand as the best wood for hurdle-making and for 'binding' traditional laid hedges.

Some trees were planted or promoted specifically for charcoal making. Pure stands of hornbeam, uncoppiced for decades, are a striking feature of Wealden woods on clay: the growth is slow and twisted, like a forest of charmed snakes, and the stems are often patterned with fine, silvery lichens. Alder ('dolly-wood'), and above all the shrub alder buckthorn, provided the best charcoal for gunpowder. The alder 'carr' at Powermill Wood nature reserve near Battle was owned by Alfred Nobel, who went on to invent dynamite and endow the Nobel Prizes.

On marshy ground, notably around Lewes, osier-beds were planted and cut each year for basket-making. There are several native forms and a bewildering array of hybrids were selected, with names such as 'Dicks', 'Kecks', 'Tulip Willow', 'Brown Merrin' and 'Mawdesley's Long Skein': all are now very rare. The bat willow - a form of the native white willow with a straight trunk and a spire-shape - is still frequently planted in the east, especially in the lower Rother valley, in wide-spaced, scintillating rows. One at great furnaces lit up the winter's night (closing down only in summer when the streams' flows became too unreliable); the forest rang to the pounding of the 5m long trip-hammers which beat the cast-iron into wrought-iron. The necklaces of lakes or 'hammer-ponds' in many valleys (for example at Leonardslee gardens) were engineered to ensure a more constant supply of water to the wheels which powered the hammers and the furnace-bellows.

Many more hammer-ponds have since run dry, their wooded beds (as at Park Wood, Hellingly) revealed by the absence of bluebells, wood anemones and other indicators of ancient woodlands, which take centuries to recolonise a disturbed soil. Many great Wealden houses, such as Batemans, Rudyard Kipling's home at Burwash, originated as iron-masters' mansions.

The explosion of the iron industry in the sixteenth century co-incided with another rise in population, when many more Wealden woods would probably have been cleared had they not been protected by the powerful interests of the

Robertsbridge, felled in 1902, had a trunk more than 2m thick and yielded over a thousand cricket bats.

The other native trees, such as birch, aspen, or crab apple, would also have had their uses: birch supplies the head and handle of a besom broom; aspen was used for shields; apple wood burns with a fumigating, balsam smell. Sometimes, though, these undesirables must have been weeded out as soon as they appeared. A woodland was the community's factory floor, with almost every twig being gathered for faggots: nothing could go to waste, and there was little room for untidiness.

Today's forester has a choice of exotic forms which grow much faster than the native trees, although their timber cannot command so high a price. A rich, moist soil is often planted with hybrid poplars, notably 'Robusta' with its ruby-red leaf-flush and 'Balsam Spire' with its heady spring perfume. Tall trees are relics from grant-aided plantings in the 1950s, when there was a big matchstick market. These trees have the advantage of being very open-crowned and not affecting the natural understorey.

In the 1950s and 60s, vast areas of natural coppiced woodland were grubbed up to make way for pulpwood conifers. The commonest trees (in descending order) are Scots pine, western hemlock, Corsican pine, hybrid and Japanese larch, Norway spruce, Douglas fir, western red cedar and Sitka spruce: lodgepole pine, which thrives in exposed, upland conditions, is seldom used. Alone among these trees, Scots pine seeds abundantly, so it can be hard to tell whether a pinewood on the greensand or on Ashdown Forest has been planted.

Great Wood, a Forest Enterprise woodland at Battle, is typical of 1950s coniferisation. Areas of chestnut coppice have been kept; the wild trees hang on along the stream and in forgotten corners. There are twelve different plantation species in small or mixed blocks, selected to suit the rapidly-changing soil types. Many grassy rides dissect the woodland, and are full of flowers such as devils-bit scabious, heath bedstraw and lousewort. A few ornamental trees have been set along them.

Sussex plantations are never the spruce monocultures of upland Britain, nor do they really resemble the dark, forbidding forests of the city-dweller's imagination. Many of the conifers have vividly beautiful bark or foliage in their own right, and attract specialist birds such as crossbill, coal-tits, goldcrests and siskins to the area; their canopies tend to support very high insect populations, on which the massed birdlife feeds. Fungi often appear particularly numerous and varied under the dense shade of hemlocks, though this is probably only because the absence of an understorey makes them easier to spot.

The terrible loss in such a woodland has been of the complex natural communities which depended on the native trees - the rare insects eating the leaves and the bluebells underneath them - and of all the accumulated evidence of the role which these trees have played in the lives of our ancestors.

Near the bottom footpath into Great Wood from Marley Lane (TQ768163), some experimental plots were established between 1985 and 1988. These include fast-growing cider gums, hybrid wingnuts, Italian alders and roblé beeches.

Elsewhere in the county, a surprising range of trees have been tried in forestry, not always with success. In exposure - notably on the seaward side of Friston Forest above Eastbourne - sycamore and Austrian pine are invaluable; Lawson's cypress is often used to 'nurse' young beech plantations. Grand fir, on a rich sheltered soil, is as fast as any tree: plantations up to 40m tall at Pickwell near Bolney were wrecked in 1987. Japanese red cedar, Serbian spruce and, as a young tree, rauli are sometimes used. Noble fir, Holford's pine and Monterey pine were all tried out in Worth Lodge Forest, but only a few specimens survive. There are young coast redwood and Leyland cypress stands at Pickwell, a Monterey cypress block in Friston Forest and a big red oak plantation in Great Wood, Stanmer.

But the joker in the pack is the horse chestnut coppice at Blackbrook Wood, Westmeston. Could it have been planted in error for sweet chestnut? Or did the owner want his woods to flower before they were cropped? Whatever the explanation, this extraordinary, knock-kneed, rickety stand goes only to show that horse chestnut - whose timber is only useful for wooden spoons and children's building blocks - does not take well to coppicing.

ironmaster. A distinction really needs to be made between the production of 'timber' and of 'wood'. Wood - for fires, fences, hurdles, or small carpentry - accounted for the main bulk of cropped material and could best be supplied by the fast-growing but manageable-sized stems of a coppice. The market for timber - for ships, mansions or churches - was more limited, but because it demanded the right kind of tree grown under the right conditions for a century a more, it was always at the mercy of social change and of fashions in forestry. Timber-consumers - the gentry, colleges or the church - have also left many more written records than the farmers and cottagers who used or burnt wood, and so, when we think of forestry, we still tend to think, for instance, of the supply of huge oak beams to the navy, even though, in terms of bulk, this market was a negligible one.

One of the best sources for really big oak logs had become the Weald (although the poor roads meant that it could take two summers to haul them to the nearest navigation). Consequently, there was some concern when suitable trees began to be felled to provide charcoal for the iron industry, and by 1585 it had become illegal for the industry to use sound oak, ash and elm trees in the Weald. Through the centuries that followed, the iron-masters saw to it that most woods became well-managed coppices, and Daniel Defoe, visiting the Weald in 1724, found it to remain 'one inexhaustible Store-House of Timber . . . able at this time to supply Timber to rebuild all the Royal Navies in Europe'.

Coppicing and wildlife

A somewhat counter-intuitive attribute of coppicing is that it has actually proved beneficial to a large and conspicuous proportion of our woodland wildlife. Within the Wildwood, butterflies would have had to travel to sunny, windblown clearings to find wild flowers in summer, and birds had to seek out dense young regrowth to conceal their nests. Marooned in tiny, isolated woods, such species could survive only if these chance patterns of clearance and regrowth happened to be regularly and reliably recreated by coppicing. During the last fifty years, many of the coppices which had been continuously worked for centuries have been neglected, developing into dense, dark, even-aged stands: nightingales and fritillary butterflies, once widespread, are now only to be found in those few woods - generally nature reserves - where coppicing still goes on. In West Dean Woods, near Chichester, the hazel is in its second 'rotation' of coppicing by Sussex Wildlife Trust volunteers. All the cut wood is sold as charcoal, firewood, wood-chip, or the stakes and whippy 'binders' used in the Sussex style of hedgelaying.

The many wild flowers safeguarded by traditional coppicing at West Dean Woods include a colony of wild daffodils.

Thanks to the depredations and disruptions of successive ice ages, there are only about 40 species of tree native to Sussex - the exact figure depends on your interpretation of 'species', 'tree' and 'native'. And, with the exception of fruit trees - apples, plums, cherries and above all pears - these were almost the only kinds to grow here into Tudor times. There were no cypresses, cedars, pines, firs, planes or horse chestnuts. It was only very slowly, in the 17th and 18th centuries, that the wealthiest landowners began to take an interest in growing the strange trees which had begun to trickle back from other parts of the globe. And it was only the mid 19th century that this trickle became a flood. The Victorian *nouveaux riches*, flocking to the romantic landscape of the High Weald, all surrounded their mansions with the kit of conifers which nurseries were now supplying: wellingtonia, Lawson's cypress, western red cedar, Corsican pine, deodar - there may have been many others, but these were the tough, long-lived species that still survive. For a genuine stately home, a full-scale pinetum now became a must.

What we think of as the 'old' Sussex gardens, such as Sheffield Park or Leonardslee, only really accumulated their wealth of rare plantings during the early years of this century, a period of great horticultural enthusiasm when Sussex gardeners were at the forefront of testing new species. Very few collections have been continuously cared for and added to over the century; but what has happened is that the opportunity to grow at least one or two rare trees - once the prerogative of the very rich - has come within the grasp of more and more people, so that the actual numbers of exciting exotic trees in the county has snowballed, with nurseries and garden centres springing up to cater for ever more adventurous and sophisticated tastes. There are now estimated to be four ornamental trees for every British citizen, the proportion in Sussex being significantly higher than this.

Sweet chestnut was one of the first trees to be introduced to Britain. The biggest today - this relatively young tree with a trunk approaching 4 metres in diameter - is at Cowdray Park.

No subject seems more likely to set gardeners, foresters and conservationists against one another than the question of whether it is native or exotic species that we should focus on planting. Native trees, the gardeners argue, spring up as weeds in their thousands as soon as their backs are turned (and if they don't, their rarity in the wild is a landscape feature we should respect). If we want to go to the trouble and expense of planting a tree, then we could do well to choose something more beautiful or more exciting than our very limited range of native species can offer.

The indiscriminate planting of exotic forms, the conservationists retort, has suburbanised many rural scenes, and does nothing to protect our fauna of often rare leaf-eating insects and insect-eating birds, for which a foreign tree might as well be made of plastic. Worse, introduced species have a tendency to outcompete their native counterparts, after the fashion of the American grey squirrel.

Both sides of this argument hold water. It would be absurd to hold that the muted, repeating patterns of our impoverished native tree-cover could be 'improved' by planting exotic species. Thanks, however, to the arboricultural enthusiasm of our predecessors, the whole of Sussex has now come to resemble nothing so much as a giant arboretum of thriving species from around the globe, and every one of these - be it a maple from Korea or an oak from Morocco, a pine from Mexico or a southern beech from Tierra del Fuego - is a

Naturalised trees in Sussex

Sycamore *Acer pseudoplatanus*. Introduced from Southern Europe by about 1500; produces seedlings by the millions which on sufficiently rich soils grow fast and can out-compete all native trees except beech. The heavy leaf-litter tends to kill off woodland flowers. Areas most likely to be over-run are ghyll woods on heavy clay or downland plantations following storm damage; a "healthy" ancient woodland can normally look after itself, perhaps with the odd sycamore tree playing the part of a well-behaved native. On the credit side, sycamore foliage supports a greater insect mass than that of any other tree, so that sycamore woods are often alive with insectivorous birds.

Cherry laurel *Prunus laurocerasus*. This looks rather like a tree-sized version of the game-covert *Rhododendron ponticum* and behaves like one too, rapidly invading moist wood-lands on clay by means of suckers and seedlings. A tree at Borden Wood is 18m tall and nearly 30m across. Nothing can survive under an established thicket and a lot of effort is spent each year on trying to control it. All parts of the plant are infused with hydrocyanic acid and the fumes from cut or burnt foliage can be highly toxic.

Portugal laurel *Prunus lusitanica*. Similar to cherry laurel but slighly less aggressive.

Scots pine *Pinus sylvestris*. A native of Scotland, but not of Sussex since about 5000BC. Re-introduced in the 18th century, it reproduces prolifically on very light soils, and is a troublesome weed in ungrazed relic heathlands.

Turkey oak *Quercus cerris*. Introduced in 1737; seeds prolifi-cally on light, sandy soils and has now established itself, notably south of Battle. It hosts alternate generations of the Knopper gall wasp, which sometimes transforms almost the whole native acorn crop into deformed and infertile galls.

Sweet chestnut *Castanea sativa*. A component of British woods since Roman times; it produces seedlings quite frequently but its abundance on sandy soils is principally due to widespread plantings and great longevity.

Apple *Malus domestica*. Descendants of orchard apples are much more common in the wild than the native crab, especially along main roads and railway lines. The leaves are hairy, the flowers tend to be pink, and the fruit are variously edible, but hybrids also occur.

Plum *Prunus domestica*. Widely but inconspicuously naturalised, especially as the variety *insititia* (bullace/ greengage).

Myrobalan plum *Prunus cerasifera*. Widely naturalised alongside bullace and blackthorn in hedges and spinneys.

Norway maple *Acer platanoides*. This maple missed being a native by a whisker, and regenerates happily but not spectacularly on clay soils; there is a notable Norway maple coppice at Dower House Farm, Blackboys.

Holm oak *Quercus ilex*. Seedlings are fairly frequent near coasts.

Snowy mespil *Amelanchier lamarckii*. Naturalised widely but not abundantly on the greensand.

Pear *Pyrus domestica*. The native status of the wild pear is uncertain; trees by lanes and in hedges with edible fruit are clearly descendents or hybrids of orchard stock.

Medlar *Mespilus germanica*. There are some old trees in woods and hedges north of Battle, where the species could conceivably be native.

Cotoneaster. Several species regenerate here, and tree-sized forms or hybrids are sometimes found in woods (normally on chalk).

Horse chestnut *Aesculus hippocastanum*. Seedlings grow up readily, but the conkers are seldom carried far from the parent.

Bird cherry *Prunus padus*. A native of Norfolk northwards, occasionally seeding and more frequently suckering in Sussex.

White poplar *Populus alba*. Sometimes establishes itself in the wild by suckering.

Grey alder *Alnus incana*. A commonly-planted southern European tree; seedlings have been known to crop up far from any plantings, for instance in the swamp at Powdermill Wood, Catsfield.

False acacia *Robinia pseudacacia*. A vigorously suckering tree; specimens cropping up in the countryside may also be seedlings. A 'sport' of the curious single-leaved form 'Unifolia' has appeared in a ditch at Marsh Farm, Binsted - a nightmare for any field botanist!

whole different world of colours, bark textures, and growth patterns, which is just waiting for you to appreciate it. Such a wealth of exotic forms is particularly valuable when it is a memorial or landmark tree that is needed and when native trees, after a few years, lose all evidence that anyone ever has planted them. However, there are regrettably few views left where non-native enormities such as Leyland cypresses or 'Kanzan' cherries are not playing an increasingly conspicuous part.

The image of exotic trees running riot and overwhelming the countryside needs to be looked at more closely. Surely planting out more than a thousand different forms and then leaving them to pollinate each other and bear seed is a bit like opening all the cage doors at London Zoo?

Bearing in mind how many trees thrive in the Sussex climate, very few indeed have proved able to reproduce themselves here. None have yet become an unmitigated ecological disaster and only five have become a real nuisance. A tree's seeds are programmed to germinate only when conditions are optimal for the growth of the vulnerable seedlings, and in the case of species from even a marginally differing climate those conditions will probably never obtain here. If we leave aside the question of whether some of our "wild" trees, such as English Elm, really are native, the box below lists the introduced species which do seem able to perpetuate themselves here, in something like a descending order of fecundity.

Swedish whitebeam *Sorbus intermedia*. Seedlings sometimes appear but I know of no mature wild trees. A sapling grew for several years out of the top of a Chusan palm in Alexandra Park, Hastings.

Fig *Ficus carica*. Occasionally forms thickets, as around the ruins of the Greyfriars at Winchelsea.

Sea buckthorn *Hippophae rhamnoides*. Occasionally behaves invasively in coastal situations.

Laburnum species. Occasionally naturalised.

Walnut *Juglans regia*. Some trees in woods and scrub are presumably self-seeded.

Sour cherry *Prunus cerasus*. A shrubby species which very occasionally naturalises.

Bay willow *Salix pentandra*. Native to northern Britain; occasional wild trees (and/or hybrids with crack willow) are seen, notably above Trotton.

Roblé beech *Nothofagus obliqua*. Fast-growing seedlings sometimes appear.

Japanese maple *Acer palmatum*. Seedlings are often found in gardens.

Bay *Laurus nobilis*. Seedlings sometimes appear.

Lawson cypress *Chamaecyparis lawsoniana*. Seedlings are numerous on mossy banks under planted trees, but seldom survive.

Norway maple *Picea abies*. Occasional seedlings.

European silver fir *Abies alba*. Occasional seedlings, mainly on greensand in the west.

Chusan palm *Trachycarpus fortunei*. Most of the trees in Leonardslee gardens are self-seeded.

Violet willow *Salix daphnoides*. Established in an old watercress bed near Burpham.

Indian horse chestnut *Aesculus indica*. The conkers germinate abundantly.

Western red cedar *Thuja plicata*. Numerous seedlings, very seldom surviving.

Western hemlock *Tsuga heterophylla*. Occasional seedlings, very seldom surviving.

Douglas fir *Pseudotsuga menziesii*. Occasional seedlings, very seldom surviving.

Monterey cypress *Cupressus macrocarpa*. Occasional seedlings.

Monterey pine *Pinus radiata*. Occasional seedlings?

Golden rain tree *Koelreuteria paniculata*. Occasional seedlings.

Cabbage palm *Cordyline australis*. Reproduces itself in very mild coastal areas (notably Alexandra Park).

Kohuhu *Pittosporum tenuifolium*. Occasional seedlings in mild areas.

Strawberry tree *Arbutus unedo*. Trees growing in unsuitable places in park shrubberies, etc. may be seedlings.

Black cherry *Prunus serotina*. Seedlings noted at Whatlington.

Common lime *Tilia x europaea*. Planted specimens are almost immortal because of their suckering habit; wild trees have been reported.

Tree of Heaven *Ailanthus altissima*. The locations of old trees at Beauport Park and some other sites are now marked by expanding groves of young suckers.

Caucasian Wingnut *Pterocarya fraxinifolia*. Suckers profusely.

Stag's-horn sumach *Rhus typhina*. Suckers profusely.

Red oak *Quercus rubra*. Suckers vigorously; may perhaps seed.

Cappadocian maple *Acer cappadocicum*. Suckers vigorously.

Caucasian elm *Zelkova carpinifolia*. Suckers vigorously.

Balsam poplar *Populus balsamifera*. Suckers vigorously.

Tupelo *Nyssa sylvatica*. Sometimes suckers vigorously.

Sassafras *Sassafras albidum*. Suckers vigorously.

Pterostyrax hispida. Suckering at Hollycombe.

Coast redwood *Sequoia sempervirens*. Two seedlings appeared under a pair of old trees in Alexandra Park, and were transplanted and have grown on. Felled trees coppice well.

Chinese white pine *Pinus armandii*. A seedling under three old trees in the pinetum at The Hyde.

Weymouth pine *Pinus strobus*. A young spontaneous tree at Hollycombe, near old plantings.

Noble fir *Abies procera*. A seedling under a big old tree at Claremont School, Hastings.

Nootka cypress *Chamaecyparis nootkatensis*. A 14m Leyland cypress growing in an old bonfire pit below the restaurant at Leonardslee is believed to be a new cross, ie. Nootka cypress pollinated by Monterey cypress.

Monkey puzzle *Araucaria araucaria*. A seedling grew up in a crack of some steps at Beauport Park at the turn of the century.

Mexican white pine. A seedling recorded in the *Sussex Plant Atlas* near Weir Wood.

Commemorative trees

To mark Queen Victoria's silver jubilee, it was decided to plant two woods on the scarp of the Downs above Streat - one in the shape of a 'V' (for Victoria), and the other an 'R' (Regina). The 'V' swallowed up 3060 trees, cost £12, 10 shillings and fourpence to plant, and, 135 years on, still cocks its two green fingers at the little folk of the Weald. Exactly the same effect would have been achieved, of course, by fencing the outline against sheep and rabbits and waiting for 20 years, but we should probably be thankful that the Victorians decided instead to plant their letter and that the cash ran out before the 'R' became a reality. The single, gigantic letter dominates this range of the Downs, making them look less like Kipling's whale-back and more like a half-submerged submarine.

Coronation Wood, Hastings

More than two thousand trees were planted around Sussex to commemorate George VI's coronation in 1937. One in ten have reached their sixtieth birthdays - which is par for the course, though nowadays we flatter ourselves that we could do better. The most ambitious scheme was Coronation Wood, adjoining Alexandra Park in Hastings, where, among 1500 trees, the oaks were raised from acorns of the noble old pollards in Windsor Great Park. Unhappily, any inherited nobility has yet to show itself.

Sweet chestnuts at Beckley church

The oldest of the magnificent sweet chestnuts around Beckley church are said to have been planted to celebrate the defeat of the Armada. As so often with such picturesque legends, the explanation seems to be prosaic: another name for the tree is 'Spanish' chestnut. They soon look much older than they really are, and the Beckley trees are unlikely to predate the 18th century. (Comparably, the big Chinese paulownia or 'empress tree' in the old St John's Road nurseries behind Warrior Square station in St Leonards is claimed to have been planted by a 19th century Chinese princess.)

Gethsemane cypresses

During a pilgrimage to the Holy Land in March 1963, led by the Bishop of Chichester, seed was collected from an Italian cypress overlooking the Garden of Gethsemane. The seedlings were planted in churchyards all over the county and have thrived remarkably well, though those at Battle and Aldwick, growing beside busy main roads, are suffering from the polluted air. The best is

The 'V' on the Downs above Streat was planted to commemorate Queen Victoria's silver jubilee.

a dense, 10m column at Thakeham church.

In 1984, the centenary of the establishment of the Greenwich meridian was marked by the ceremonial planting of a wellingtonia on the line by the 'tree warden' of each High Wealden parish; holm oaks were planted in the Low Weald and over the Downs. (The East Sussex tree wardens, whose role is to catalise local interest in caring for and planting trees and to provide on-the-ground support for district tree officers, were the first ever. Now most counties have adopted the scheme.) To mark the millennium, a whole line of trees across the country is conceived.

The poignancy of a commemorative tree lies in its very *raison d'être*: it long outlives the memory of whoever, or whatever, it was planted by or for. This book is filled with wonderful trees which were planted by people who evidently knew and loved them, but about whom I have been able to discover nothing else, so that we no longer know whom we have to thank.

Dizzy heights: this grand fir was planted by Benjamin Disraeli to commemorate his visit to Eridge Park in 1868 and, 130 years on, is the tallest tree in Sussex. (The favourite pastime of his great political rival Gladstone was cutting trees down.)

Dutch Elm Disease

Scientists have counted the pollen grains from different kinds of trees buried in dated sediments, and found that six thousand years ago the percentage of elms in the Wildwood plummetted and never really recovered. It seems likeliest that they were the victims of an early outbreak of Dutch Elm Disease (DED).

DED is caused by a microscopic fungus which infects the tree's sap-transmitting vessels and whose spores get carried from tree to tree on the mouthparts of bark-boring beetles (*Scolytus* species). To isolate the infection, the elm shuts off its vessels and anything above the blockage is starved to death. An elm, however, is a difficult tree to kill outright: healthy suckers will continue to appear from the roots of a tree whose crown has been killed off, and these will not be infected with DED until the stems are big enough to interest the beetle again (at about 10cm diameter).

The disease itself is nothing new. An epidemic in the 1930s killed off millions of trees to ground level, and in 1954 Esther Meynell was lamenting 'the decline of elms in the rural landscape [of Sussex].' But then, in the mid 1960s, a far more virulent form of the fungus entered Britain on elm logs from America. From one of its points-of-origin, at Southampton, the new pathogen raced eastwards into Sussex , destroying almost all the trees in its path.

33

The 'Preston Twins' at Preston Park, saved by Brighton's DED control programme, are believed to be the oldest and largest English elms left in the world.

Elms are the grandest and noblest of all native trees. English elms have been recorded as much as 45m tall. The famous 'Doctor's Tree' by the Brighton Road in Crawley (named after Dr Robert Smith who lived in the adjacent Tree House in the 1790s) was 21x590@0m in 1838, and its hollow, paved interior was used as the town lock-up: its remains were finally blown down in 1935. With the exception of the wych elm, elms are not really woodland trees, but do best standing singly in fields or lined along hedges. They shrug off salt gales and urban pollution and thrive on raw chalk.

The specimens lost in the late 1960s were, consequently, the most conspicuous trees on the coastal plain, while their importance around the windswept Downs of East Sussex was even greater. In the poor soils of the Weald, by contrast, they were thinly scattered. By 1969, the epidemic had crossed the county boundary into East Sussex and the county council made a monumental decision: to take all possible steps to control the disease within the Downs and the downland towns by immediately felling any infected trees and burning their bark, by trenching around their roots to isolate them and by injecting landmark trees with fungicide. For over twenty years, this programme was co-ordinated by Tony Denyer, whose role in saving the elm in Sussex has been immense.

Characteristically contorted growth of *Ulmus glabra* 'Serpentinei' in Church Road, St Leonards: an early victim of DED.

The control area has now been extended as far as the Adur in West Sussex, and is administered by the Sussex Downs Conservation Board.

Outside the oasis of the eastern Downs, the disease was left to run its course, reaching Rye in the early 1980s. Nearly all the elms of West Sussex and of the East Sussex Weald have now gone underground as shrubs, throwing up suckers which are killed off in turn when they grow big enough. How long they can keep up this resistance is unclear.

Within the control zones, constant vigilance was needed from a team of patrol officers. Infection could flare up in some remote copse or back garden and spread outwards in a matter of days. Much-loved trees had to be ruthlessly felled as soon as the tell-tale wilting of a branch-tip was spotted. Casualties mounted through the 1970s: 1979 was the worst year with over five thousand trees having to be removed, and a strategic retreat was made from the downs south of Lewes as the epidemic got out of hand. Since then, infection rates have fallen and by 1994 were outstripped by the growth of old suckers to tree size; 1997 was the quietest year since the campaign began. The success of the programme has led to similar schemes being adopted in many other British towns.

Perhaps the best hope for the elm's long-term future lies with the old strain of the disease, which kills some trees while allowing others to recover. Although it is less virulent than the new strain, it has not been wiped out by it: indeed, it seems to have the competitive edge and may, given time, squeeze out its deadly cousin.

The evening of Thursday, 15th October 1987 began much like any other. Commuters parked their cars under the elms of Brighton or the limes of Forest Row. Foresters dreamed happily of their burgeoning larch poles, whilst conservationists fretted about the gloom of neglected coppices. Gardeners congratulated one another upon their prime tree specimens, and forecasters promised a quiet 24 hours. The NUM came into possession of a new country house headquarters at Buxted Park, with its well-timbered grounds.

By six the following morning all had changed. The Great Storm, sweeping across south-east England and exiting into the North Sea all during the space of the small hours, had miraculously claimed only five Sussex lives. But for every human living in the county, eight trees had been blown down.

Four kilometers of railway track at Wadhurst, always a blackspot for leaves on the line, now had 74 tree-trunks as well. The National Trust's Slindon Beechwood - the most celebrated 18th century plantation in the country, like a towering Gothic cathedral - had been reduced to matchwood, with the few, shattered snags that were still vertical seeming only to emphasise the enormity of the loss. The unique avenues of tall yews at Close Walks Wood at Midhurst were largely gone, as was the beech tree planted on the high altar of Bayham Abbey (probably by Humphry Repton in 1805) which used to crown the vista down the nave. Landscapes in which foresight had combined with centuries' growth, such as Ashburnham Place and Sheffield Park, lay in ruins.

Approximately one tree in five in Sussex had been destroyed by the storm, the percentage being higher among notable specimens which were often at the end of their lives in any case. However, exceptionally vigorous specimens had generally survived, including nearly all the biggest and tallest trees. Species with very long-spans also fared well: the wellingtonias, coast redwoods, planes, ginkgos and yews. The windblow had been particularly bad because soils were soft and wet after a period of very heavy rain, so that species adapted to wet conditions - alder, willow, poplar, swamp cypress - also tended to remain upright, though many alders and poplars snapped off. The shallow-rooted trees of lighter soils were worst hit - notably beeches, silver firs and spruces. Some trees survived the storm only to succumb to the less severe gales of January 1990, when the losses were largely of specimens which had stood for two years in unaccustomed isolation, or with weakened root-systems.

The storm of 1987 was a disaster for most people who experienced it, and, you might think, represented an unqualified loss for anyone who cared for trees. In fact, writing ten years on, it seems that the benefits have clearly outweighed the sacrifices. Although some gardens lost more than half their best or most striking trees, others were scarely touched, and revisiting them heart-in-mouth in the 1990s, it was often astonishing to find what was still there and what was missing. But even the barest vistas offered opportunities for new plantings and new designs where none may have existed before. In the countryside at large, most landscapes were changed, though the memories soon faded and conspicuous trees, grown in exposure, tended to be the ones that survived.

By the early 1990s, the most telling evidence of what had happened lay in the lost limbs and shattered crowns of the remaining trees, everywhere transforming the old, tranquil picture of comfortably-rounded treetops into a restless and jagged scene of change.

The storm did a lot to alert people to the value and vulnerability of trees, and hundreds of thousands of pounds of much-needed funds suddenly became available for woodland management and parkland restoration through the Government's Task Force Trees initiative. Most importantly of all, perhaps, the storm represented instant coppicing for many dark and neglected woods, and sunlight reached the ground for the first summer in decades; butterflies, bluebells and breeding birds all experienced a bonanza.

Patcham Place, Brighton, after the 'hurricane' of October, 1987.

The future

And what of the next hundred years? The 20th century has witnessed an explosive enthusiasm for tree-planting coupled, tragically, with a loss of native tree-cover: at first the catastrophic sacrifices to coniferisation and intensive agriculture, and more recently the insidious depletions due to new housing and bypasses. Humans today can transmit a library of information around the globe in the twinkling of an eye, but to recreate a vanished ancient woodland in so short a spell as a century is far, far beyond us.

Very recently nature conservation has begun to shift its focus away from the struggle to prevent more losses, towards defining a positive agenda of reconstruction and recovery, as spelled out in Sussex Wildlife Trust's *Vision for the Wildlife of Sussex*. Dr Tony Whitbread, the Trust's head of conservation, has floated the idea of rebuilding a New Forest or even a Wildwood on the greensand hills, by linking together all the pieces of ancient woodland and wooded common that remain into a block large enough to sustain minimal human interference and ultimately, perhaps, to support bison, beavers or wolves.

Sustainable forestry

At a time when 90% of Britain's timber is imported, and valuable upland habitats are being sacrificed to coniferisation so that the wood can be transported south again, it has been estimated (1983) that only a fifth of the annual increment of timber in East Sussex is being harvested. Much of this is locked away in small Wealden woods with difficult access, but where the wildlife (not to mention the forester) would unquestionably benefit from coppicing and structured tree-felling. David Saunders, East Sussex County Council's Trees and Woodlands Officer, has long been a passionate advocate of the sustainable use of local, high-quality native hardwoods. The Weald Woodfair, an annual event, celebrates the uses of native timber and helps bring buyers and potential suppliers together.

Trees in towns

For all the wealth of rare young trees in private gardens, trees in towns are having a hard time of it. The value of town trees is incalculable: they carry a wealth of wildlife with them; they baffle traffic noise; they cool and sweeten the summer air and deflect winter gales; and they isolate tonnes of dust and toxic fumes from the atmosphere.

Tolerance of nearby trees differs remarkably among homeowners from one part of Sussex and another, but the trend is now one of increasing mistrust and alarm. A tree is much bigger than we are. It is long-lived, and in some important ways it remains a free spirit, outside our control. Cowboy tree-surgeons conjure visions of storms which will smash small trees through roofs twice their height away; insurance brokers grill their clients over the possibility of subsidence, and a magnificent Hungarian oak, growing on a not very shrinkable soil on the verge of Dunnings Road, East Grinstead, was hacked back recently because of the fears of a homeowner living 30m away.

Ease-of-maintenance and sunshine are valued more than peacefulness and verdure; everywhere, and at great cost, small-growing and graceful trees such as birches have their heads unceremoniously lopped. 'Proper' trees are exiled to the countryside and year by year the grey-brown urban roofscape becomes blanker and emptier. Street-trees are threatened by cable-laying and exhaust emissions and show, too, an unforgiveable tendency to shed messy, mushy leaves on cars and pavements in the autumn. Casualties are replaced, if at all, by toy trees such as flowering cherries or crabs. Trees in urban parks are constant prey to vandals, so have to be quick-growing, tough and preferably thorny. Less and less is there the confidence to plant a tree that will need a century's peace to perfect itself. When did you last see a sapling cedar of Lebanon?

The vulnerability of trees

One day, Mr and Mrs Tree decide to plant an arboretum. The arboretum, to begin with, has a thousand trees, but unfortunately the Trees' understanding of aftercare is not equal to their original enthusiasm. A hundred trees lose out in competition with mown grass, fifty are barked by rabbits, and fifty succumb to drought during their first summer. A few are unsuitable and are repeatedly frosted or fight a losing battle against air pollution. The gardener kills a hundred by scraping their trunks all round with his gang-mower, and a hundred more by taking the bark off with his strimmer. Fireblight, honey fungus and insect attacks all take their toll.

Over the years that follow more fatalities occur, including those of Mr and Mrs Tree themselves. The arboretum is overwhelmed with ash and sallow seedlings, which outcompete some smaller trees and kill them. After 50 years many of the maples, cherries and apples are beginning to pop off from old age. After 70 years only 150 of the original 1000 trees remain, though many of these are very rare and some are the biggest in Britain. Half of these are blown down the next year by a freak storm. After 90 years all the rest of the trees are lost when planning permission is granted for an out-of-town superstore on the site - including the yew, which had just celebrated the tree equivalent of its fourth birthday.

Trees are among the very few organisms which can outlive ourselves. The idea of a 500-year-old oak is wonderful - as, for that matter, is the idea of a 130-year-old oak. But the potential longevity of trees, as well as inspiring awe and respect, blinds us to the fact that they are always growing, and always vulnerable. The life-expectancy of any tree at planting is much less than a person's, and the only way to guarantee that we bequeath the same rich legacy that we have inherited is to care for the trees around us, and to keep on planting more.

Tree Superlatives

Rare Trees

Wild black poplar at Sheffield Bridge.

The status in the wild of many of the 1000 species of tree cultivated in Sussex gardens is hard to determine: some may be on the brink of extinction. What is clear is that generations of keen gardeners have quite inadvertently built up a living, genetic reservoir of world-wide importance: several trees which are popular in Britain, including the Serbian spruce, Monterey cypress and metasequoia, are known to have only tiny and vulnerable populations in their native countries. *Franklinia alatamaha*, a flowering tree of the tea family, was found by the botanist John Bartram in about 1765, in an area of woodland of no more than a hectare by the Altamaha River in Georgia. It has not been seen in the wild since 1790 and the few trees in cultivation all originate from seed raised by John and his son William at their garden in Pennsylvania: Terence Devonport has a thriving young specimen in his arboretum at Peasmarsh Place. *Betula uber*, the Virginian round-leaved birch, was thought to have become extinct until a few trees were found along Cressy Creek in Virginia in 1975. A world-wide regeneration programme was instigated and there are now two trees in the birch collection at Wakehurst Place. The Sicilian Fir *(Abies nebrodensis)* , which is represented by mature trees of two slightly different forms at Borde Hill and Leonardslee, once grew in great forests but by the 1970s had been reduced to a mere 17 trees on Mount Scalone, with a handful in botanic gardens worldwide. The American sweet chestnut, *Castanea dentata*, is practically extinct in the wild because of chestnut blight. A single healthy tree in Warren Wood at Borde Hill was blown down in 1987 but was not removed and, in its horizontal position, remains very much alive.

Among native trees, the most threatened group is currently the elms. Even before the current outbreak of Dutch Elm Disease, some distinct and native clones and hybrids were probably growing unrecognised here, but in very small numbers. The genealogy of willows is equally confused; the almond willow and purple osier are rare in the wild (though the purple osier has a weeping form which is now sometimes planted in gardens). The hybrid between these species, *Salix x mollissima*, was found during recording for the *Sussex Plant Atlas* only once, at Amberley Wild Brooks.

A number of microspecies of service tree are native to north and west Britain. A splendid tree in Hastings cemetery (by the back fence above Ivyhouse Lane) has the slender-based leaves and clear orange berries of *Sorbus bristoliensis*, a form found wild only in Leigh Woods and Clifton Down near Bristol. How it should have come to be planted in Hastings is one of the many mysteries of dendrology. Another specimen of known origin was planted at Wakehurst Place in 1992.

The black poplar (*Populus nigra* subsp. *betulifolia*) is a questionably native tree of which only a handful of old examples are known in Sussex, though it has become quite widespread recently. Cuttings taken from the very characterful old trees at Sheffield Bridge and Isfield church are now growing at Wakehurst Place. Another tree being propagated at Wakehurst is the Plymouth pear, *Pyrus cordata*, which is known in Britain only from a few hedges in the south west.

Tall Trees

There are 32 trees in Sussex currently believed to be 40m or more tall. The figure of 40m is arbitrary (although it does represent the height at which most trees will begin to find it difficult to transport water to their tops in the rainfall regime which Sussex enjoys). Every one of these 32 trees, however, is a conifer from the Rocky Mountains, and four of the five species are also the tallest trees now left in the world.

The roll-call is the same as in Great Britain as a whole (where the higher rainfall and the shelter of the Scottish glens allows the trees to grow very much taller than they can in Sussex), but Sussex is at the limit of the climatic conditions which these conifers need, and the tallest trees in all the central and eastern English counties will belong to quite different species, such as common lime, London plane and black Italian poplar.

The county's tallest trees are all in the sheltered valleys of the High Weald or on the very suitable soils of the green-sand in the west - with the notable exception of St Roche's Arboretum, in a dry valley of the chalk: the size which the Douglas firs and coast redwoods have reached here could not have been predicted, and it is hard to anticipate until you are among them, as the site is so completely hidden among the hills.

At least eight trees of four different species have reached 46-47m in Sussex during this century, but this height has never apparently been exceeded.

This grand fir on the Hollycombe estate is likely to become the tallest tree in Sussex early in the 21st century.

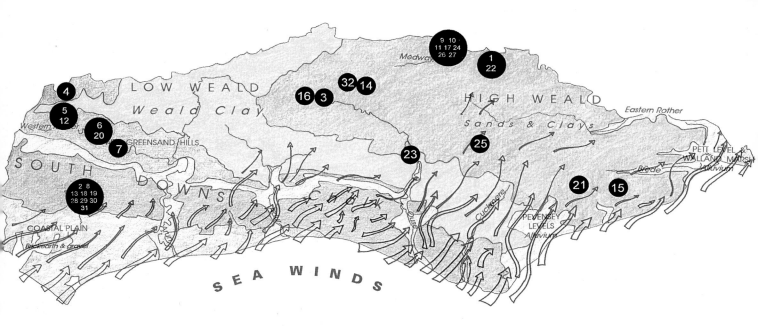

The county's tallest trees:

1 Grand Fir *Abies grandis* Eridge Park 46x142(94). Nearly dead at the top (which was partly blown out in 1987) but growing vigorously from about 42m; was 47m in 1984.

2 Douglas Fir *Pseudotsuga menziesii* St Roches Arboretum 44x124(97). On the north side of the valley-bottom, next to the taller coast redwood; was 47m in 1954.

3 Wellingtonia *Sequoiadendron giganteum* Nymans 43x209(97) Currently regrowing a top killed off by lightning; was about 47m a few years ago, and 31m in 1931.

4 Grand Fir *Abies grandis* Hollycombe estate 43x150(97). This tree was struck by lightning a few years ago but is currently growing at least 50cm a year, so, barring disasters, should take over the mantle of the tallest tree in the county in a few years. It grows in a sheltered valley under the Greensand scarp near Upper Wardley, and may have the potential to grow much taller.

5 Coast Redwood *Sequoia sempervirens* Keeper's Farm 43x144(97). A magnificent tree growing with two others in an open field in the Milland Vale.

6 Grand Fir *Abies grandis* Cowdray Park 43x136(97). Above the pond in the valley; was 46m in 1984 but lost most of its top in 1987. It is regrowing vigorously from 41m.

7 Grand Fir *Abies grandis* Selham House 43x130. Unlike the other very tall trees, this grows on a low ridge and is a conspicuous landmark in the western Rother valley.

8 Douglas Fir *Pseudotsuga menziesii* St Roche's Arboretum 43x125(97). On the north side of the valley-bottom; was 47m in 1954.

9 Wellingtonia *Sequoiadendron giganteum* Highfields Park 42x178(94). The wellingtonia avenue, high on a hillside, dominates the upper Medway valley.

10 Wellingtonia *Sequoiadendron giganteum* Highfields Park 42x168(94). In the avenue.

11 Wellingtonia *Sequoiadendron giganteum* Highfields Park 42x156(94). In the avenue.

12 Coast Redwood *Sequoia sempervirens* Keeper's Farm 42x137(97).

13 Douglas Fir *Pseudotsuga menziesii* St Roche's Arboretum 42x124(97). On the south slope of the valley.

14 Douglas fir *Pseudotsuga menziesii* Stonehurst 42x124(97). In the valley; now rather exposed and beginning to die back.

15 Wellingtonia *Sequoiadendron giganteum* Beauport Park 41x258(97). In Ring Wood; planted 1856?

16 Wellingtonia *Sequoiadendron giganteum* The Hyde 41x247(96). In the pinetum.

17 Wellingtonia *Sequoiadendron giganteum* Highfields Park 41x182(94). In the avenue.

18 Coast Redwood *Sequoia sempervirens* St Roche's Arboretum 41x154(97). On the north side of the valley-bottom.

19 Douglas Fir *Pseudotsuga menziesii* St Roche's Arboretum 41x146(97). Dead at the top.

20 Wellingtonia *Sequoiadendron giganteum* Cowdray Park 40x237(97). In the avenue.

21 Wellingtonia *Sequoiadendron giganteum* Normanhurst Park 40x231(94). Below Model Farm.

22 Wellingtonia *Sequoiadendron giganteum* Eridge Park 40x199(94). In Mill Wood.

23 Wellingtonia *Sequoiadendron giganteum* Newick Park 40x189(94). In the dell by the house.

24 Wellingtonia *Sequoiadendron giganteum* Highfields Park 40x166(94). In the avenue.

25 Wellingtonia *Sequoiadendron giganteum* Possingworth Park 40x165(94). In the pinetum.

26 Wellingtonia *Sequoiadendron giganteum* Highfields Park 40x158(94). In the avenue.

27 Wellingtonia *Sequoiadendron giganteum* Highfields Park 40x146(94). In the avenue.

28 Douglas Fir *Pseudotsuga menziesii* St Roche's Arboretum 40x132(97). Dead at the top.

29 Douglas Fir *Pseudotsuga menziesii* St Roche's Arboretum 40x132(97). Dead at the top.

30 Douglas Fir *Pseudotsuga menziesii* St Roche's Arboretum 40x124(97). Dead at the top.

31 Douglas Fir *Pseudotsuga menziesii* St Roche's Arboretum 40x124(97). Dead at the top.

32 Western Hemlock *Tsuga heterophylla* Wakehurst Place 40x118(97). Near the top of Westwood Valley.

Big trees

Fifty nine trees are currently known in Sussex with trunks more than 250cm in diameter - the size of a small room. Not all these trees are ancient. More than a quarter are wellingtonias, which were introduced only in 1853 and within a few decades are bound to dominate any list of this kind. It is worth remembering, however, that Sussex, with its ancient parks, hedges and woodlands, has more really big, old trees than most European countries can boast. The greatest concentration of large boles is on the greensand in the west, although wellingtonias tend to grow slightly faster in the High Wealden soils.

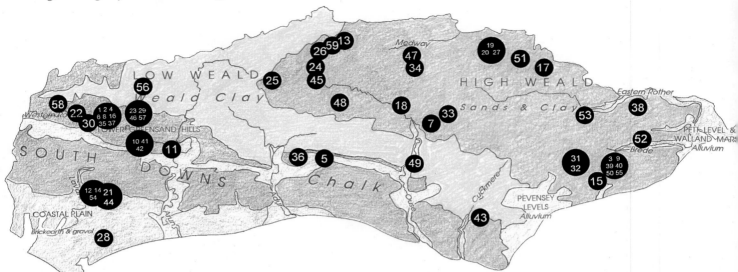

1 Sessile Oak *Quercus petraea* Cowdray Park 8x389@1.8m(97). 'The Queen Elizabeth Oak' - a very hollow pollard perhaps 800 years old.

2 Sweet Chestnut *Castanea sativa* Cowdray Park 25x364@0.4 - 2m(97). In the same field as the Queen Elizabeth Oak; the tape is deflected under one huge, broken limb.

3 Monterey Cypress *Cupressus macrocarpa* Beauport Park 17x325@0.2-1m(97). Planted around 1843 on the Roman road to the Beauport Bloomery.

4 Sessile Oak *Quercus petraea* Cowdray Park 9x319@0.5m(97) Next to the Queen Elizabeth Oak and very burry.

5 English Oak *Quercus robur* Danny 14x315@0m- 1m(97). By the drive. An ancient tree of which two fragments remain, diverging from the base.

6 Wellingtonia *Sequoiadendron giganteum* Cowdray Park 30x310(97). The end tree in the avenue, planted in 1871.

7 Wellingtonia *Sequoiadendron giganteum* Rocks Park School 34x306(98). Less buttressed and more massive than its rival at Cowdray.

8 Sweet Chestnut *Castanea sativa* Cowdray Park 26x305(97). By the A272, next to the drive to Moor Farm. Unlike most other big chestnuts, it has a smooth, tapering bole.

9 Monterey Cypress *Cupressus macrocarpa* Beauport Park 20x304@0.5m(97). Planted around 1843.

10 Sweet Chestnut *Castanea sativa* Burton Park 21x301(97). By the bend in the drive to the Lodge Green development; forks at 3m.

11 Yew *Taxus baccata* Coldwaltham church 14x296(97). The oldest and most impressive of all the Sussex churchyard yews.

12 Cedar of Lebanon *Cedrus libani* Goodwood 32x292@0.5m(97). Behind the cricket pavilion, planted in 1761.

13 Sweet Chestnut *Castanea sativa* Windfalls x290(93). A beautiful tree with a smooth trunk.

14 Cedar of Lebanon *Cedrus libani* Goodwood 23x289@1m(97). By the cricket field, planted in 1761; has a very impressive bole.

15 Yew *Taxus baccata* Crowhurst church 12x289@0.8-1.5m(98).

16 Sweet Chestnut *Castanea sativa* Cowdray Park 19x286(97). A gnarled tree by the house drive.

17 English Oak *Quercus robur* Whiligh 10x285@1m(95). A very old oak, apparently featured in a manorial map of 1493.

18 Wellingtonia *Sequoiadendron giganteum* Sheffield Park 35x284(94). North of the Second Lake; the tape has to be deflected above a massive burr on the south side.

19 Beech *Fagus sylvatica* Eridge Park 26x284@1.1m(94). An ancient pollard on the footpath from Frant village.

20 Beech *Fagus sylvatica* Eridge Park 31x284@0.8m(94). A boundary-bank pollard in Rocks Wood, with a very gnarled bole.

21 Sweet chestnut *Castanea sativa*. Halnaker Park 27x282(98). East corner; bole 7m long.

22 Yew *Taxus baccata* Stedham church 11x282@0m(97).

23 English Oak *Quercus robur* Petworth Park 23x279(97). Outside the Pleasure Grounds; the oak with the most impressive clean bole in the county.

24 Wellingtonia *Sequoiadendron giganteum* Tilgate Forest Lodge 37x277(96). The largest of three.

25 English Oak *Quercus robur* Coolhurst 18x276@1m(96). The Sun Oak, the cottage next to it once being the Sun Inn; very spreading and vigorous.

26 Wellingtonia *Sequoiadendron giganteum* Tilgate Park 33x275(96). Near the Inn; planted around 1876.

27 Beech *Fagus sylvatica* Eridge Park 32x275@0.7m(94). In White Hill wood.

28 Monterey Cypress *Cupressus macrocarpa* Crimsham Manor 15x275@1m-1.5m(97).

29 English Oak *Quercus robur* Petworth Park 18x274(97). West of the Lower Pond. Very hollow; the tape is run around two separate fragments of trunk.

30 Cedar of Lebanon *Cedrus libani* Ashfield House 30x272 @0.5m(95). Taped between branches.

31 Wellingtonia *Sequoiadendron giganteum* Normanhurst 36x271(94). Planted about 1872.

32 Wellingtonia *Sequoiadendron giganteum* Normanhurst 38x270(94). Planted about 1872.

33 Wellingtonia *Sequoiadendron giganteum* Buxted Park 31x270(94). Above the trout pond.

34 Wellingtonia *Sequoiadendron giganteum* Ashdown Park Hotel 28x269@1.2m(94) The tape is deflected under one low limb.

35 Sessile Oak *Quercus petraea* Cowdray Park 20x269@1.2m (97). On the golf course.

36 Sweet Chestnut *Castanea sativa* Bishops 13x269@0.6m(97). The bole above 0.6m is swollen by big burrs.

37 Wellingtonia *Sequoiadendron giganteum* Cowdray Park 30x268(97). In the avenue, planted 1871.

38 English Oak *Quercus robur* Higham House, Northiam 30x268(94). An ancient pollard.

39 Monterey Cypress *Cupressus macrocarpa* Beauport Park x267@0.3m(92). Planted around 1843; nearly dead.

40 Monterey Cypress *Cupressus macrocarpa* Beauport Park 26x265@0.3m(92). Planted around 1843; nearly dead.

41 Sweet Chestnut *Castanea sativa* Burton Park 19x265@1m(97). Towards Burton Mill Pond from the drive to Lodge Green.

42 English Oak *Quercus robur* Burton Park 15x265@1m-2m(97). Below the Lodge Green development.

43 Yew *Taxus baccata* Wilmington church 14x265@0.2m(94). Two trunks from low down.

44 Sweet chestnut *Castanea sativa* Halnaker Park x265@1.2m (98). South corner; a few live sprouts.

45 Cedar of Lebanon *Cedrus libani* Nymans 23x264@0m(96). On the house lawn, with many trunks from the base.

46 English Oak *Quercus robur* Petworth Park 18x263@1m(97). Below Upperton; measured under massed burrs on the trunk.

47 Beech *Fagus sylvatica* Broadstone Warren 32x262(94). Just off the track north from the Ashdown Forest centre; massive, burred bole.

48 Wellingtonia *Sequoiadendron giganteum* Cuckfield church 26x262@0.5-1.5m(96.) The tape is deflected under a big low limb.

49 Cedar of Lebanon *Cedrus libani* Wellingham House 19x259@0.3m(94). Many trunks divide from the base.

50 Wellingtonia *Sequoiadendron giganteum* Beauport Park 41x258(97). Planted in 1856?

51 Wellingtonia *Sequoiadendron giganteum* The Mount 34x258(94).

52 Hornbeam *Carpinus betulus* Brede 16x258@0.5m(97). A mass of fused trunks in an ancient hedge-line.

53 English Oak *Quercus robur* Glottenham Farm 9x257(94). A very gnarled old tree, growing half in the farmyard duck-pond.

54 Cedar of Lebanon *Cedrus libani* Goodwood 21x256@0.8m (97). On the golf course, planted in 1761; very spreading.

55 Wellingtonia *Sequoiadendron giganteum* Beauport Park 39x254(97). Ring Wood; planted in 1856?

56 Wellingtonia *Sequoiadendron giganteum* Ebernoe House 31x253(97).

57 Sweet Chestnut *Castanea sativa* Petworth Park 22x253(97). On the hilltop outside the Pleasure Grounds.

58 Wellingtonia *Sequoiadendron giganteum* Dangstein 32x252(97).

59 Small-leaved Lime *Tilia cordata* Worth 23x252(93). A magnificent pollard, on the Worth Way east of the church.

The oldest and largest English oak known in Sussex is at Whiligh, near Wadhurst.

Above left: 130 feet of candles on the tallest known horse chestnut, at Screens Wood, Arundel.
Above: Enormous hazel at Forest Row.
Left: A house holding an umbrella. The champion Keaki (*Zelkova serrata*) was planted at Lower Sherriff Farmhouse, near Horsted Keynes, from seed collected in Japan in 1890.

Within Easy Reach

*H*ere are the finest tree collections and woodlands which can be visited in each part of Sussex. (Sometimes the trees are labelled; sometimes a sense of adventure is needed to hunt them out.) Turn to the *Gazetteer* for more details of the whereabouts of each site and for an index of the notable individual trees.

Anyone who understands the harm done to trees and the environment by vehicle exhausts and road-building schemes will probably prefer to visit these places, as I have done, by public transport. For each entry here the nearest train station or regular bus-stop is given, whenever the trees are a short or pleasant walk away. (Locations served by train are invariably served by local buses.) East Sussex and West Sussex County Councils each publish bus and rail maps of their areas, as well as area timetable books giving full details of all bus services in the county.

Many of our Sussex gardens are also set in glorious countryside, and the more adventurous will sometimes be able to incorporate their visit in the course of a country walk, using the county's vast and excellently-maintained network of public footpaths and long-distance trails.

Arundel ↓

Arundel Castle (regularly open). Train: Arundel.
Denmans, Fontwell (open daily). Bus: Fontwell; Eastergate.

Battle ↓

Ashburnham Place (parkland open days). Bus: Ninfield (Standard Hill).
Beauport Park (footpath from Black Horse Hill). Bus: Black Horse Hill.
Normanhurst Park (1066 Way from Catsfield). Bus: Catsfield.
Powdermill Wood (nature reserve). Pleasant country walk from Battle Abbey. Train: Battle.

Some useful telephone numbers

East Sussex County BusLine   01273 474747 or
                              01797 223053
West Sussex Traveline   0345 959099

These helplines can answer all your local bus timetable enquiries, with detailed information about how to reach your destination, including bus and train connections.

For journeys in the Brighton and Hove area, information, maps and timetables are available from:

Brighton & Hove Bus & Coach Company
                              01273 886200

Information about trains is available from:
National Rail Enquiry Line   0345 484950

Bexhill ↓

Bexhill Cemetery. Bus: St Mary's Lane.
Crowhurst church (ancient yew). A pleasant country walk from either Bexhill or Battle.
High Woods, Pear Tree Lane, Bexhill (nature reserve). Bus: Pear Tree Lane.

Bognor Regis ↓

Hotham Park (public). Train: Bognor Regis.

Brighton and Hove ↓

Preston Park (public). Bus: Preston Road.
Royal Pavilion grounds (public). Train: Brighton.
St Anne's Well Gardens (public). Bus: Seven Dials.
Stanmer Park (public). Train: Falmer; bus: Sussex University.
Withdean Park, London Road (public). Bus: Withdean.
Woodvale Crematorium. Bus: Lewes Road, Brighton.

Chichester ↓

Bishop's Palace grounds (public). Train: Chichester.
Cookscroft (open days). Bus: Somerley.
Goodwood (open access).
Jubilee Gardens (public). Train: Chichester.
Kingley Vale, near West Stoke. (nature reserve).
Lavant church (ancient yew). Bus: Lavant.
Stansted Park (regularly open). Train: Rowlands Castle (walk through Stansted Forest).
Tangmere church (ancient yew). Bus: Tangmere.
West Dean Gardens /St Roche's Arboretum (regularly open). Bus: West Dean Gardens.
West Dean Woods (nature reserve). Bus: West Dean; below South Downs Way.

Crawley ↓

Broadfield Park (public). Bus: Broadfield.
The High Beeches (regularly open). Bus: Handcross.
Milton Mount Gardens (public). Bus: Pound Hill.
Nymans (open daily). Bus: Handcross.
Snell Hatch Cemetery. Train: Ifield.
Tilgate Park (public). Bus: Tilgate.

Crowborough ↓

Crowborough Warren Pinetum (open access).
   Bus: Crowborough (walk through Ashdown Forest).
Eridge Park (garden open days and footpaths).
   Bus: Eridge Green; Frant.
Penns-in-the-Rocks (open days). Bus: Mott's Mill Corner.
Rotherfield church (ancient yew). Bus: Rotherfield.
Warren House (open days). Bus: Crowborough.

East Grinstead ↓

Duckyls House (open days). Bus: Turners Hill.
Gravetye Manor Hotel. Bus: Turners Hill.
Kidbrooke Park, Forest Row (open days). Bus: Forest Row.

Eastbourne

Hampden Park (public). Train: Hampden Park station.
Wilmington church (ancient yew). Bus: Wilmington.

Hailsham ↓

Herstmonceux Castle (regularly open). Bus: Windmill Hill.
Park Wood, Hellingly (nature reserve). Bus: Amberstone
   Corner; Hellingly.

Hastings & St Leonards ↓

Alexandra Park (public). Bus: St Helens Road.
Gensing Gardens (public). Train: Warrior Square.
Hastings Country Park. Bus: Fairlight.
Linton Gardens (public). Train: Hastings.
St Helens Wood (nature reserve).

Haywards Heath ↓

Borde Hill (open daily). Train: Haywards Heath.
Stonehurst, Ardingly (open days). Bus: Wakehurst Place.
Wakehurst Place, Ardingly (open daily). Bus: Wakehurst
   Place.

Horsham ↓

Architectural Plants Nursery, Nuthurst.
Horsham Park (public). Train: Horsham.
Leonardslee, Lower Beeding (regularly open).
South Lodge Hotel, Lower Beeding.
Warnham Court, Warnham (open days projected).
   Train: Warnham.

Lewes ↓

Ashcombe Bottom (footpath). Below South Downs Way
   at Blackcap.
The Railwayland Local Nature Reserve. Train: Lewes.
Southover Grange Gardens (public). Train: Lewes.

Midhurst ↓

Cowdray Park (garden open days and footpaths).
   Bus: Cowdray Park.
Hollycombe (Steam Collection regularly open).
   Train: Liphook.
Hurst Mill (open days).
Malt House (open days). Bus: Trotton.
Petworth Park (open access). Bus: Petworth.
Rooks Clift, near Treyford (public footpaths). Below
   South Downs Way.

Stedham church (ancient yew). Bus: Stedham.

Pulborough ↓

Coates Manor (open days). Bus: Fittleworth.
Cedar Tree Cottage (open days).
   Bus: Sullington Warren; Rock.
Coldwaltham Church (ancient yew). Bus: Coldwaltham.
The Mens (nature reserve).

Robertsbridge & the Rother Valley ↓

Ewhurst church. Bus: Ewhurst.
Fontridge Manor (open days). Train: Etchingham.
Mountfield Court (open days). Bus: John's Cross.
Northiam church (ancient yew). Bus: Northiam.
Pashley Manor (regularly open).

Uckfield ↓

Buxted Park (hotel and footpaths in park). Bus: Uckfield.
Sheffield Park (open daily).

Worthing ↓

Highdown (public). Train: Goring.
Worthing Crematorium. Bus: Worthing Crematorium.

**The oldest known Apollo fir, at Tilgate Park in
Crawley, is one of many great Sussex trees which can
easily be visited using public transport.**

The Sussex Tree List

This is not a complete list of tree species growing in Sussex, less still of all the noteworthy specimens. It features only those forms which have already reached tree-size (that is, with a distinct trunk at least 15cm thick), excluding some particularly obscure kinds and many more found growing only as saplings. Relative abundances of each form are suggested by "abundant", "frequent", "occasional" or "rare": "rare" implies that fewer than five examples have been found.

The opening measurements under each species are of the current Sussex 'county champions'. The first is the tallest known example (if two or more trees tie, the one with the biggest bole is preferred). The second is the tree - if different - with the largest known bole (measurable at 1m or above); where an inflated measurement of a short or branchy bole, measured below 1m, is significantly greater, this is given next. Where a measurement is also the largest currently known in Great Britain and Ireland, it appears in bold. Measurements of any other nationally important, or locally conspicuous, specimens then follow. Planting dates ('p1800') are included where these have been documented. Full locations of all the sites featured in this list are given in the Gazetteer, along with details of their accessibility to the public.

European Silver Fir *Abies alba* Occasional as an old tree, mainly on greensand in the west. Eridge Park (Pinetum, p1883) dying back from 40x116(94); St Roche's Arboretum (bottom glade) 38x91(97).

SILVER FIRS

Dizzie's green fingers

The **silver firs** tend to be aristocrats among trees, ornaments of the stateliest homes: expensive to obtain, slow to establish, choosy about conditions, but then growing rapidly into huge trees with boles like temple columns and needles etched with precious metals. (The Caucasian fir has recently come into favour as an up-market Christmas tree).

Being rather short-lived and vulnerable to wind-throw and pollution, they are one of the few groups of trees which are no longer represented by such fine specimens as 50 years ago.

Two European silver firs (Abies alba) were planted in Oaters Wood in Cowdray Park in about 1733; in 1906 Elwes and Henry measured the larger at 40x98. The beeches which had drawn it up had then just been felled, allowing them to take its photograph; but, they predicted, it was now 'likely to be blown down by the first severe gale'. It died, quietly of old age, around 1973.

The tallest tree in Sussex in 1998 (p 33) is a grand fir (Abies grandis) planted by Benjamin Disraeli when he stayed at Eridge Park in 1868 - clearly the man had green fingers.

The Pinetum was once full of trees planted by the Abergavenny's illustrious guests. It is situated on a gentle north-east slope among tall woodlands in the most sheltered corner of the county, but lacks any over-riding reasons why this and other trees should have grown so tall. In 1908, it had reached 23m; in 1957, it was 46m, and had run into the glass ceiling for heights in the climate of south-east England. It is the slender tree with the tilted top which is

conspicuous on the skyline as you travel south out of Tunbridge Wells on the A26.

One of the most august trees in Sussex is the Apollo fir (Abies cephalonica var. apollinis) in Tilgate Park, a poised, columnar fir about 200m south of the 'Inn in the Park'. This tree from the mountains of Greece (p. 46) was planted in or around 1876, and is the oldest piece of evidence we have for the cultivation of the form in Britain.

Lovely Fir *A. amabilis* At Leonardslee (Camellia Walk, young tree): 15x20(96).

King Boris' Fir *A. borisii-regis* Rare; collections. Wakehurst Place (back drive) 22x123(97).

Santa Lucia Fir *A. bracteata* Rare; collections. Wakehurst Place (Horsebridge Woods, leaning) 27x69(97).

Grecian Fir *A. cephalonica* Occasional as an old tree in W. Warninglid Grange 29x117(96); Nymans (long woodland walk, very broad) 23x122(97); Stansted Park (S end of Arboretum, monstrous broken tree) 28x120(97).

Apollo Fir var. *apollinis* Occasional. Tilgate Park (S of Inn, p1876?) 29x108(96); Borde Hill (Warren Wood, slender) 28x61(95).

A. chensiensis At Borde Hill: Gores Wood 16x26(96), Tolls (hung up and died back) 13x33(95).

Cilician Fir *A. cilicica* Occasional: collections. Malt House (Pinetum, ?) 29x68, 28x61(97); Wakehurst Place (garden fence S of Westwood Valley) 24x45(97).

Colorado Fir *A. concolor* At Tilgate Forest House: 13x61@0.5m(96).

Low's White Fir var. *lowiana* Occasional - large and some small gardens. Leonardslee (Top Garden) 33x89(96).

'Violacea' Occasional (several small gardens). Denmans 13x40(97).

A. fargesii At Pickwell (?) 8x19(96).

Momi Fir *A. firma* Occasional: collections. Brook House (died back) 21x51(93); Wakehurst Place (Pinetum) 21x47(97).

var. *tardiva* At Borde Hill (Gores Wood): 24x53(95).

Forrest Fir *A. forrestii* Occasional: collections. Malt House (Pinetum) 16x32(97); Wakehurst Place (Horsebridge Woods/Bloomers Valley) 13x40(97).

Grand Fir *A. grandis* Occasional, mostly as a young tree (gardens, plantations). Eridge Park (Pinetum) 46x142(94); Hollycombe (footpath above Home Farm) 43x150(97); Brook House (Seven Acre Wood, died back from 40m) 38x109(97); Worth Lodge Forest (in plantation) 36x78(96) - and see 'Tall Trees'.

FIRS

• *The Korean fir's small size and abundant purple cones make it uniquely suitable for the small garden*

Nikko Fir *A. homolepis* Occasional: collections. Wakehurst Place: Horsebridge Woods 28x74, below Pinetum 17x74(97); Warnham Court (school) 25x64(93); Leonardslee (Hill Garden+) 25x56(96); Alexandra Park (Thorpe's Wood, p1935) 16x67(93).

var. *tomomi* Rare: Borde Hill (Warren Wood) **22x61**(95); Wakehurst Place (Pinetum) 20x45(97).

Korean Fir *A. koreana* Occasional: some small gardens. Borde Hill (Gores Wood) 11x22(95).

Red Fir *A. magnifica* Rare: collections. Wakehurst Place (Horsebridge Woods, young tree) 10x25(97).

Sicilian Fir *A. nebrodensis* At Borde Hill (back of Tolls, p1940): 14x32(95).

var. *mattei* At Leonardslee (below house): **15x36**(96).

Caucasian Fir *A. nordmanniana* Occasional - sometimes as young tree in small gardens. Eridge Park (lake dam) 37x72(94); Tilgate Park (lakeside, p1895?) 35x101(96); Cowdray Park (top of gardens) 35x95, 35x79(97).

Algerian Fir *A. numidica* Occasional: collections. Wakehurst Place: Horsebridge Woods 27x87, Pinetum 19x82(97); Borde Hill (Warren Wood) 25x76(95).

Hedgehog Fir *A. pinsapo* Occasional. Knepp Castle (Pleasure Grounds) 27x88(96); Malt House (Pinetum, leaning) 27x66(97); Christ's Hospital (branchy, p1902?) 18x66(97).

'Glauca' At Stansted Park (Arboretum, E fence): 14x45(97).

Noble Fir *A. procera* Occasional: in a few small gardens; mostly as 'Glauca' (grafted). Worth Abbey 34x100(96); Trotton Place 28x129(97); Park Grove 32x122(94); Sheffield Park (Top Lake) 31x119(94); Claremont School 33x112(94).

Min Fir *A. recurvata* Rare: Wakehurst Place (Pinetum) 16x47(97); Borde Hill (Gores Wood, Wilson's seed) 16x39(95).

A. sachalinensis var. *nemorensis* At Borde Hill (Gores Wood): 15x31(95).

Himalayan Fir *A. spectabilis* At Wakehurst Place (Pinetum, branchy): 14x57@1m(97).

Veitch's Fir *A. veitchii* Occasional; collections. Hollycombe (railway, unusually thriving) 20x48(97).

Mimosa *Acacia dealbata* Occasional in small gardens, seldom surviving long. Henmer Cottage (spreading tree aged 8) 10x26(97).

MAPLES

Acer amplum At Borde Hill (Naldred Farmhouse, roadside, p1937): **13x43**(95).

A. argutum At Borde Hill (Stonepit Wood, p1932): 9x24@1.2m(95).

Trident Maple *A. buergeranum* Occasional; collections. Borde Hill: North Park cottage garden 13x57@0.5m, Stonepit Wood 10x36(95); Cowdray Park (garden by Wellingtonia avenue) 9x47@0.4m(97).

Field Maple

Field Maple *A. campestre* Native: abundant except on acid soils; a much-planted amenity tree. Arundel Castle (bottom of castle bank behind Stew Ponds) 24x61(97); Heaven Farm (nature trail) 6x112(94); Borde Hill (W side of Stonepit Wood, magnificent tree) 19x101@0.9m(95); Hurst Green (TQ739266) 17x100@1m(96); Eridge Park (fine parkland tree, above lake) 17x92(94); Arundel Park (dry valley NE of Swanbourne Lake) 22x86(96).

'Elsrijk' Occasional as young street tree. Mill Bay gardens 11x17,10x19(98).

'Pulverulentum' Rare. Lorien 8m(94).

'Schwerinii' Rare. Stanmer Park (Arboretum, p1964) **9x16**(94).

Gardeners' pets

*The **maples** can offer such a range of accessories - green bark with white stripes; red, peeling, bark; autumn colours in gold, scarlet or crimson; spring foliage in shrimp-pink or orange with purple stripes; and red, yellow or purple flowers - that they now grow in Sussex gardens in a greater variety than any other kind of tree.*

The native field maple, like most in its family, is a neat tree, never gigantic, but colourful in autumn; it is common enough in the clay of the Weald or the richer downland soils, but is something of a Cinderella, often overlooked and sometimes crowded - none of which can be said for its cousin the sycamore.

From the tree-measurer's perspective, both are damp squibs in Sussex, where no really respectable specimens have been recorded. This is curious, as the greensand hills in Kent have always boasted a number of the biggest in Britain.

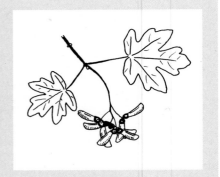

Red Snake-bark Maple *A. capillipes* A few in big gardens; more widespread as young tree. Stonehurst (Wild Garden, pond) 10x21(97); Stanmer Park (drive near fork) 8x25(94).

Cappadocian Maple *A. cappadocicum* Frequent: an amenity and garden tree. The Heath (Perrymount Rd side) 22x69(96); Jubilee Gardens, Chichester 17x87(97); Cripps Lane, Steyning (bank at bottom, bushy) 17x94@0.3m(96).

'Aureum' Occasional in gardens - far fewer than in Kent. Jubilee Gardens, Chichester 16x65(97); Waikiki 15x66(96).

var. *sinicum* Rare. Highdown (Chalk Garden, E side, p1910) 8x26(97).

Hornbeam Maple *A. carpinifolium* Occasional; collections. Wakehurst Place (above Pinetum) 9x23@1.2m(97); Borde Hill (Stonepit Wood) 6x28@0.5m(95).

Vine Maple *A. circinatum* Occasional; collections (but one in a country hedge at Barnham Lane, SU962047). High Beeches 10x21++(94).

A. cissifolium Occasional; collections. Wakehurst Place: N of Slips 9x43@0.1m(97), behind Heath Garden (dying back) 7x39@1m(91); Hurst Mill (below tennis court, lovely tree: spread 14m) 8x33@1m(97).

A. x coriaceum At Borde Hill (W of Stonepit Wood, handsome tree): 11x42(95).

Père David's Maple *A. davidii* Several large and small gardens (quite frequent as young tree); a few amenity plantings. Stonehurst (lawn below house, dying back) 15x28+26(97); Wakehurst Place (specimen beds, 'George Forrest') 12x52(97); Stanmer Park: nursery beds ('George Forrest') 10x37, behind house ('Ernest Wilson') 9x32(94); Duckyls Wood ('George Forrest', dying back) 13x37+20(96); Hotham Park (by house, p1987) 9x19(97).

Horned Maple *A. diabolicum* Rare. Alexandra Park (Thorpe's Wood, p1935) 10x32(93).

f. purpurascens Rare. Borde Hill (Naldred Farmhouse by road, ivy-clad, p1909) 10x**43**(95).

A. x dieckii At Tilgate Park (mid S, branchy): 15x39@0.6m(96).

Lime-leaved Maple *A. distylum* At Lorien: 10x15(94).

A. erianthum Rare. Borde Hill (W of Stonepit Wood, p1932) 8x**30**@0.9m(95).

A. fulvescens At Borde Hill (Park N of Azalea Ring, p1932): **13x50**@0.7m(95).

Amur Maple *A. ginnala* Occasional - some small gardens. Fontridge Manor (Arboretum): 11x19@0.9m, 9x20(94); Upper Beeding (street planting) 6x31@0.4m(96).

A. grandidentatum Rare. Brantridge Park 7x28@0.5m(93).

Paper-bark Maple *A. griseum* Occasional: many well-planted gardens. Borde Hill (Naldred Farmhouse road side, dying back, p1912) 12x37@1.2m(95); Highdown (Middle Garden, p1912) 9x40(93); Leonardslee (drive) 11x53@0.5m(96); Preston Park (Preston Road) 9x49@0.4m(94).

A. heldreichii In Jubilee Gardens, Chichester: 12x25(97).

Balkans Maple *A. hyrcanum* Rare. Alexandra Park (below bandstand, S bank) 8x25(93).

Downy Japanese Maple *A. japonicum* At Wakehurst Place: above Pinetum **12x43**, Entrance Grounds 9x47@0.2m(97).

'Aconitifolium' Occasional: old rockeries etc. Wakehurst Place (Coates Wood) 8x**28**+27++(97); Leonardslee (N of Loderi Garden) 8x31@0.2m(96).

Full Moon Maple 'Vitifolium' Occasional in big gardens. Borde Hill (Stonepit Wood, top) 9x**56**@0.2m(95).

Lobel's Maple *A. lobelii* Occasional street and park tree; now planted much more. Borde Hill (W of Stonepit Wood, dying back) 22x108@0.8m(95); Patcham Place Recreation Ground (back bank) 19x37(94); Lucastes Avenue, Haywards Heath (one of four) 15x43(97).

Oregon Maple *A. macrophyllum* Occasional: collections. Hollycombe (railway) 17x73(97); Beauport Park (Oak Wood, much died back) 9x58(97).

A. miyabei At Borde Hill (Stonepit Wood): 11x36(95).

A. mono Occasional: collections. Borde Hill (Stonepit Wood) 11x36(95).

var. *tricuspis* At Borde Hill (Stonepit Wood): 11x36(95).

Montpelier Maple *A. monspessulanum* Occasional; collections. Borde Hill (Stonepit Wood; Corsican seed, 1932) 12x42(95).

Box Elder *A. negundo* Frequent, mostly in small gardens (reversion from 'Variegatum'?) Little Clevelands 15x66 and 14x66@1m(97); Petworth Park (Pleasure Grounds) 15x58(97).

'Auratum' Rare. Castle Place, Lewes 9x30; Stanmer church 7x19(94).

'Pseudocalifornicum' At Borde Hill (North Park below Azalea Ring, p1927): 10x53(95).

'Variegatum' Quite frequent - smaller gardens. Hampden Park (bog garden) 15x36(94).

var. *violaceum* Occasional. Sunte Avenue, Lindfield 9x40.

Black Maple *A. nigrum* At Borde Hill (North Park behind cottages, dying back, p1911): 13x41(95).

Nikko Maple *A. nikoense* Occasional: big gardens. Borde Hill (Stonepit Wood) 13x35@1m and 11x42@l.lm (95); Nymans (House Drive) 13x48@0.3m(96).

A. oliverianum Rare. Borde Hill (Gores Wood) 8x19(95); Hurst Mill (over stream) 6x15(97).

Italian Maple *A. opalus* Occasional: big gardens. St Roche's Arboretum (S slope, biggest of many) 22x96@1m(97).

Japanese Maple *A. palmatum* Frequent: large and many small gardens in various forms (eg 'Osakazuki'). Borde Hill (Azalea Ring) 12x33(95); Leonardslee (N of Loderi Garden) 11x43(96).

'Albomarginatum' At Leonardslee (below Cross Paths): 9x30@1m(96).

'Amoenum' At High Beeches (The Glade): 10x28(94).

Purple Japanese Maple f. *atropurpureum* About as frequent as the type. South Lodge Hotel (rockery) 11x43@0.9m(96); Hollycombe (estate; split in half and decaying) 9x**57**@1m(97).

'Aureum' Rare. Gravetye Manor (East Garden) 7x28@1.2m ++(97).

'Dissectum Atropurpureum' Frequent: rockeries. Holmbush (drawn up) 5x16(96).

'Hagoromo' Rare. Chelwood Vachery 7x18@0.3m(94).

'Kagiri Nishiki' Occasional in big gardens - quickly reverts. Leonardslee (below Cross Paths) **12x34**(96).

'Linearilobum Atropurpureum' Rare. Leonardslee (N of Loderi Garden) 9x29(96).

'Reticulatum' At Leonardslee (below Cross Paths): 10x28+16(96).

Moosewood *A. pensylvanicum* Occasional; big gardens. St Roche's Arboretum (valley floor, mid) 9x23(97); Stonehurst (Wild Garden, S) 9x23(97).

Norway Maple *A. platanoides* Abundantly planted in steets and parks; naturalising. Christ's Hospital (Foxes) 26x65; Petworth Park (Upper Pond dam, fine tree) 20x**127**(97); St Cuthmans School (bridlepath N of school) 25x114@0.9m(97).

'Crimson King' Probably frequent, but hard to tell from the commoner 'Goldsworth Purple'. Stanmer Park (Arboretum, p1964) 12x27(95).

'Cucullatum' Rare. Alexandra Park (by tearooms) 17x75(93).

'Drummondii' Abundantly planted but quickly reverting. West Stoke House 13x46(97); South Pond, Midhurst 10x36(97); Friary Lane carpark, Chichester 12x30(97) - all largely reverted.

'Goldsworth Purple' Becoming abundant in small gardens (including unlabelled 'Crimson King' and 'Faasen's Black'). Stedham Mill (N bank, in woods) 15x45(97); Pound Hill (A264 street planting) 13x47(97); Denmans 12x47(97); Withdean Park 15x44(94).

'Palmatifidum' Occasional (including all cut-leaved forms). Titmus Drive, Tilgate (street tree) 12x44(96).

'Schwedleri' Frequent as an older park and street tree - rare in the east. St Roche's Arboretum (SE edge) 23x65(97); Christ's Hospital (best of many) 21x87(97); Sheffield Park (by Cascade) 20x114@0.3m(94); Brook Street Recreation Ground 21x84(94).

'Stollii' In Steyning recreation ground (a sport?): 11x46(96).

Sycamore *A. pseudoplatanus* Not native, but growing abundant except on sandy soils. West Dean Gardens (W end of park) 30x136(97); Coolhurst (house lawn) 24x167@0.8m(96); Beauport Park (by 9th fairway) 26x143@1m(92).

'Brilliantissimum' Frequent in smaller gardens. Warnham Court (wild garden) 13x33@1.2m(97).

Corstorphine Plane 'Corstorphinense' Occasional as old tree. Pine Grove, Crowborough (wood by road) 21x63(94).

- *The horned maple gets its name from the devil's horns which sprout between the wings of its seeds*

- *With its peeling, cinnamon bark and autumn scarlet, the paper-bark maple is one of the most sought-after garden trees*

- *Lobel's maple is unusual in being a wild tree with a narrowly upright shape. It is now much planted in streets and car parks*

- *People tend not to think of maples as flowering trees, but the massed spring flowers of the Italian maple are as yellow as daffodils*

Norway maple

Sycamore

MAPLES

• *Uniquely, purple sycamore leaves are only coloured underneath, giving the tree a striking maroon tinge. Tracts of Beauport Park are turning this colour through natural regeneration*

'Leopoldii' Rare. Stanmer church (carpark) 9x33(94).

'Nizetii' Rare. Fisher's Hill 12x35; Knockbridge House 11x31@1.2m(94).

'Prinz Handjery' Occasional in smaller gardens. Leonardslee (below new house, p1930) 9x**47**@1m(96).

Purple Sycamore f. *purpureum* Frequent park and street tree; often appearing in the wild and in plantations. Wakehurst Place (top of Pinetum) **25**x110(97); Nymans (North Park) 24x88@1m(96).

'Variegatum' Frequent; a popular street tree; a wild sport at Beauport Park. Westfield Place 22x120@0.9m(94); Chithurst Monastery 20x80(97).

Golden Sycamore 'Worleei' Quite frequent: parks and streets. Wakehurst Place (head of Bloomers Valley) **21**x96(97); Butler's Green (field by A272, fine tree) 14x88(96); Ardingly recreation ground (best of three) 14x63(96); Myrtle Rd, Crowborough 13x61(94).

A. pseudosieboldianum Rare: collections. Borde Hill (Pirates Adventure) 7x15(96); Penns-in-the-Rocks 7x15@0.1m(94).

Red Maple *A. rubrum* Frequent: parks and big gardens. Hollycombe (woods near entrance to Steam Collection, with 8m bole) 26x97(97); Cowdray Park (garden) 21x85(97); South Hill (roadside) 16x78(96).

'Columnare' Occasional (including all fastigiate clones). Milton Mount Gardens (by St Catherine's Rd) 13x27(97).

'October Glory' Occasional as a young tree. Wakehurst Place (Entrance Grounds) 10x16(97).

'Schlesingeri' Rare. St Roche's Arboretum (S/mid) 11x20(97).

A. rufinerve Occasional in big gardens. Tilgate Park (below walled garden, nearly dead, ?) 11x45@1m(96).

Silver Maple *A. saccharinum* Frequent: parks and belts. Christ's Hospital (best of many) 30x122(97); St Cuthmans School (bridlepath N of school) 27x**136**(97); Gravetye Forest (Hotel drive) 29x70(97); Borde Hill (Park N of Azalea Ring) 27x119(95).

f. *laciniatum* Frequent amenity tree (mostly 'Weirii'?). Borde Hill (North Park by barn) 26x99, 19x101(95).

Sugar Maple *A. saccharum* Occasional: big gardens. Hollycombe (estate) 22x102@0.5m, 19x79(97).

Cretan Maple *A. sempervirens* Rare: collections. Highdown (Middle Garden, W) 6x19++(97).

Golden Moon Maple *A. shirasawanum* 'Aureum' Occasional - big and well-planted gardens. Leonardslee (drive by rockery, dying back) 9x31@0.1m(96).

A. stachyophyllum At Borde Hill (Gores Wood): 11x20(95).

A. sterculiaceum At Wakehurst Place (Slips): 6x15(97).

Birch-leaved Maple *A. tetramerum* Rare: collections. Borde Hill (Gores Wood) 10x19(95); Nymans (Wild Garden) 9x20(96).

A. trautvetteri Occasional: big gardens. Borde Hill (N of Tolls, p1927) 17x68(95); Wakehurst Place (Slips/Pinetum) 16x60++(97).

Rough-barked Maple *A. triflorum* Rare. Shawcross House 9x**45**(94).

A. truncatum Rare: collections. Borde Hill: W of Stonepit Wood 12x39, N Park cottage garden 11x43(95); Hurst Mill (below tennis court) 10x24(97).

A. ukurunduense At Borde Hill (Gores Wood, ?): 8x20@1m(95).

A. velutinum Rare: collections. Borde Hill (NW of Stonepit Wood, hybrid?) 13x68(97).

var. *vanvolxemii*. Rare: collections. Borde Hill: below lake dam 14x36+32(95), S of Tolls 13x47(96).

A. villosum At Nymans (Wild Garden, two trees): 9x16(96).

A. wilsonii At Warnham Court (wild garden): 6x18@1.2m(97).

A. x zoeschense Rare: collections. Leonardslee (Camellia Walk) 15x28+27+26(96).

• *The Cretan maple is the only evergreen member of the group which grows in Sussex*

HORSE CHESTNUTS & BUCKEYES

Aesculus x arnoldiana At Wakehurst Place (behind Specimen Beds): 5x19@1m(97).

A. assamica At Oaklands Park, Chichester (young tree, behind theatres): 7x16(97).

Californian Buckeye *A. californica* Occasional; large gardens. Windlesham House School (track to W) 6x17@1m(96); Iden church 5x15(94).

Red Horse Chestnut *A. x carnea* Frequent as an older amenity tree. Stansted Park (entrance, in group) 19x76(97); Rocks Park School 14x99@1.2m(94); Hartfield church (gate) 14x85(94).

'Briotii' Has now replaced the type. St Cuthmans School (bridlepath N of school, ?)15x**97**(97); Hardham church 11x72(97).

Yellow Buckeye *A. flava* Occasional: parks and collections. Goodwood (W drive) 16x33(97); Alexandra Park (over stream from bowling green) 14x64@1.2m(93); Beauport Park (caravan park)16x44(82); Ansty recreation ground (?) 11x37(96).

f. *virginica* Occasional. Alexandra Park (bank by bowling green, one of three) **20**x53(93); Bishop's Palace (huge, three-trunked tree) 17x**112**@0.4m(97).

Ohio Buckeye *A. glabra* Rare. Brighthelm Centre garden 11x32(94); Borde Hill (Pirates Adventure) 8x43(95).

Horse Chestnut *A. hippocastanum* Abundant everywhere. Screens Wood (tallest in line) **39**x144(97); Cowdray Park (A272 just W of garden, dying back) 22x184@1m(97); West Dean Gardens (park, E) 17x175@1.2m(97); St Roche's Arboretum (N of bottom entrance, forks) 31x171@0.5m(97); Chailey (field W of church, fine tree) 20x168@1m(94); Arundel Castle (path to Keep) 28x166@1m(97); Great Barn (cut back) 14x167(97).

'Baumannii' Occasional amenity tree, but quite numerous in Haywards Heath. Alexandra Park (above tearooms) 24x100(93); Littlewood 20x86(97).

'Digitata' On Hartfield village green: 8x35(94).

'Pyramidalis' Rare amenity tree. Mason Road, Southgate 11x38(96).

Piggy-back tree

Probably the tallest **horse chestnut** in Britain (p. 44) is one of a line of old trees in Screens Wood on the Downs west of Arundel, just above where the footpath crosses the deep valley.

It is very slender, and the others in the line have all been broken by storms, so that the strange impression is of a tree riding piggy-back on the shoulders of others.

('Nice horse chestnut,' I said to myself, seeing the top of it in the distance during a tour of the area in 1997. 'Not worth detouring to measure, though.'

Fortunately, I then proceeded to get lost.)

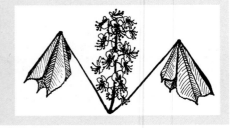

Indian Horse Chestnut *A. indica* Occasional: some amenity plantings and large gardens. Stonehurst (Wild Garden, three trunks) 21x100@0.3m(97); Ewhurst church 14x67@1m(94); Alexandra Park (Thorpes Wood, p1935) 16x65(93); Linton Gardens (best of several) 17x58(93).
'Sydney Pearce' At Wakehurst Place (behind Specimen Beds): 8x28@0.5m(97).
Crimson Buckeye *A. pavia* Occasional in large gardens. Nymans (house drive) 11x31(96); Preston Rockery (bushy) 9m(94).
A. x plantierensis Rare. Oathall Avenue roundel, Haywards Heath (very pale pink flowers; with two 'Baumanii') 14x39, 13x45(96); Stanmer Park (Arboretum, p1964) 13x42(95); Ewhurst church (pink-flowered seedling from *A. x carnea*) 12x28++(94).
Japanese Horse Chestnut *A. turbinata* Rare: collections. Wakehurst Place (Slips/Pinetum) 14x65(97); Borde Hill (by carpark) 14x47(95).
A. wilsonii Rare: Borde Hill (Lullings Ghyll, p1926) 12x30(95); Wakehurst Place (Slips/Pinetum) 10x45@0.2m(97).

Tree of Heaven *Ailanthus altissima* Quite frequent: streets (notably Worthing) and gardens. Stanmer Park (house) 25x107(94); Westgate, Chichester (back garden of 27, trimmed back) 17x**146**(97); Seaford College (behind House, several trunks) 18x149@0.3m(97).
'Erythrocarpum' Rare. The Hyde **23x134**(96).
'Pendulifolia' At Borde Hill (lakeside): 7x22(95).
A. giraldii At Borde Hill (N of Lullings Ghyll): 14x23(96).

Italian Alder *Alnus cordata* In collections, but now frequent as street tree. Borde Hill (under lake dam) 24x83(95); Alexandra Park (model railway, leans) 20x66(93).
A. firma Rare. Hollycombe (railway) **13x46**@1m(97).
Alder *A. glutinosa* Native; abundant except on dry sites; seldom planted. Old Roar Ghyll (above road bridge) **30**x47(94); Beauport Park (Swan Pond) 17x122(92); Snailham Hill 15x110@1.2m(93).
'Imperialis' Occasional. South Pond, Midhurst 13x22++, 12x23+(97).
f. *lacera* An old tree at Alexandra Park (model railway) has leaves with rounded, oak-like lobes. 21x75@0.8m(93).
'Laciniata' Occasional. Bentley Wildfowl Reserve (Canal Pond line) 13x43, 12x46(95).
A. hirsuta At Borde Hill (Stonepit Wood): 17x32, 16x43(95).

Feet in the water

The Wealden ghylls have long boasted the tallest **alders** in Britain, though the individual, thin, leggy trees tend not to survive for long in the constantly-shifting soils. The combination of wet clay with towering trees on either hand is unusual, since alder is characteristically a gregarious small tree of open river-banks.

A 100-year-old alder planted in Alexandra Park (just below the miniature railway) with rounded, oak-like lobes to its leaves, is probably unique in Britain, though similar forms (f. lacera) are said to occur naturally in Scandinavia.

Grey Alder *A. incana* Abundant: orchard shelterbelts etc. Steyning recreation ground (stream) 16x38(96); Penns-in-the-Rocks (lakeside) 12x41(94); Bognor Regis cemetery (branchy) 12x62@0.3m(97).
'Aurea' At Hurst Mill (mill race): 9x15(97).
'Laciniata' Rare. Stanmer Park (Arboretum, p1964) 10x23(94).
'Ramuleis Coccineis' At Borde Hill (Stonepit Wood): 11x17(95).
A. inokumai At Wakehurst Place (Coates Wood, young tree): 9x20(97).
A. japonica Rare. Wakehurst Place (Bethlehem Wood) 13x34(97).
Himalayan Alder *A. nitida* Rare. Warnham Court (roadside by paddock) 14x35(97).
Oriental Alder *A orientalis* At Borde Hill (S of garden, p1940, ?): 11x30(95).
Oregon Alder *A. rubra* Collections and occasional shelterbelts. West Dean Gardens (water garden) 17x47(97).
A. x spaethii Rare. Borde Hill (Stonepit Wood, splendid straight tree, p1938) **25x73**(95).
Caucasian Alder *A. subcordata* Rare. Nymans (Rose Garden) 17x55(96); Wakehurst Place (Slips/Pinetum, p1976) 16x59(97).

Snowy Mespil *Amelanchier lamarckii* (and other species?) Abundant in small gardens; naturalised on greensand, mainly S of Pulborough. Ashburnham (walk S of Broad Water, in line) 12x24++(94); Sheffield Park (path to First Lake) 6x**41**(94).

Monkey Puzzle *Araucaria araucana* Frequent: small and large gardens. Fair Oak **31**x92(97); Beauport Park (Bishops Wood) 25x104(97); Eridge Green (park lodge) 22x103(94).

Grecian Strawberry Tree *Arbutus andrachne* At Highdown (NE, p1925): 6x19(97).
Hybrid Strawberry Tree *A. x andrachnoides* In many gardens as young tree; the old large one is by Queen Street bridge, Arundel: 10x59@0.5m(96).
Madrona *A. menziesii* Occasional in big gardens. Borde Hill (Gores Wood) 15x50(95); Petworth Park (by house) 13x57+52(97).
Strawberry Tree *A. unedo* Quite frequent: old shrubberies and as a young plant. East Marden (back garden) 10m; Rye cemetery (drive) 8x44(94); Hove Recreation Ground (SE entrance) 7x41+(94).

TREE OF HEAVEN

ALDERS

• *Unique nodules on the roots of alder trees contain bacteria which 'fix' nitrogen, so that the trees supply the soil with essential nutrients*

The tallest known alders, in Old Roar Ghyll, Hastings.

MONKEY PUZZLE

STRAWBERRY TREES

Summit Cedar *Athrotaxis laxifolia* Occasional: big gardens. Duckyls Wood **20**x64(96).
King Billy Pine *A. selaginoides* Rare: collections. Wakehurst Place (Mansion lawn) 11x41(97).

A Tasmanian mystery

The **summit cedar** (Athrotaxis laxifolia), is, in its native Tasmania, a rare and generally stunted tree of the high mountains. In Britain, it was long held only to do well in the far west, where an old tree at Scorrier House, Cornwall, is 18m tall. In Duckyls Wood, however, sheltered by old oaks and vigorous Douglas firs and hemlocks, four young trees, first recorded in 1996, are already taller than this and growing fast: they clearly know why, but they aren't telling.

Chilean Incense Cedar *Austrocedrus chilensis* Rare: collections. Borde Hill (Gores Wood, fine dense column) 13x33(96).

Azara microphylla Occasional. St Roche's Arboretum (bottom glade) 9x19@1.1m(97); South Bersted church hall 8x20(97).

BIRCHES

• **Birches are grown primarily for their bark colour: white, yellow, orange, pink or, in the river birch, black and curling**

Chinese Red-barked Birch *Betula albosinensis* Rare: collections. Borde Hill (South Park, Borde Hill Laneside) 11x28(95).
var. *septentrionalis* Occasional: large and some small gardens. Borde Hill (Gores Wood) 14x25(95); Stonehurst (S end of Wild Garden) 11x26(97).
Yellow Birch *B. alleghenensis* Occasional: larger gardens. Tilgate Park (mid S) 20x79@0.5m(96); Wakehurst Place (S of Westwood Valley) 14x44(97).
B. coerulea-grandis At Wakehurst Place (Bethlehem Wood): 9x19(97).
B. costata Rare; collections. Sheffield Park (S of Second Lake): 8x18(94).
B. davurica At Wakehurst Place (Bethlehem Wood): 8x20(97).
Erman's Birch *B. ermanii* Occasional: bigger gardens. High Beeches (Queen Mary's Walk, hybrid?) 18x43(97); Borde Hill (Gorse) 14x58@1.2m(95).
var. *communis* At Wakehurst Place (Bethlehem Wood): 8x15(97).
B. ermanii x pendula Several trees are apparently this hybrid. Borde Hill (Gorse) 17x55(95).
B. ermanii x pubescens Two huge trees at Hollycombe (railway): 19x**142**@0.4m and 19x**79**@1m(97).
Japanese Cherry Birch *B. grossa* At Wakehurst Place (Bethlehem Wood): 6x15(97).
Japanese White Birch *B. japonica* Rare: collections. Alexandra Park (Thorpe's Wood, p1935) 13x**47**(93); Stanmer Park (Arboretum, p1964) 13x29(95).
B. x koehnii Rare: collections. Banks Farm 7x17@1.2m(94).
Sweet Birch *B. lenta* Occasional: larger gardens. Tilgate Forest Lodge (Middle Wood) 15x25++(96).
B. maximowicziana Occasional as young planting. Leonardslee (below Cox's Walk) 16x37(96).
B. medwediewii Occasional. Preston Park (Manor end) 7x23@0.9m(94).
River Birch *B. nigra* Occasional; less rare as young tree. Hurst Mill (below tennis court) 16x36(97).
Paper-bark Birch *B. papyrifera* Frequent as street and park tree and in big gardens. Warnham Court (Wild Garden, planted as var. *kenaica*) 21x36(97); Borde Hill (Garden of Allah) 18x72(95).
var. *subcordata* At Wakehurst Place (Bethlehem Wood): 9x20(97).
B. payprifera x utilis var. *jacquemontii* A lovely tree at Coates Manor, donated by Roy Lancaster: **12**x**41**(97).
Silver Birch *B. pendula* Native; abundant and abundantly planted, except on chalk and heavy clay. Leonardslee (W of New Pond, in park) 27x83(96), Nymans (Wild Garden) 24x79(96).
'Fastigiata' Rare. Alexandra Park (model railway) 23x**64**(93); Wildpark, Moulsecoomb (NE by Lewes Rd) 13x26(95).
Swedish Birch 'Laciniata' Occasional as young garden tree. Sheffield Park (E of First Lake, p1910) 25x42, 23x44(94).
Purple Birch 'Purpurea' Occasional as young tree. Brands 12x17.
'Tristis' Dramatically weeping trees are likely to be this clone. Silver Lane, Billingshurst (street planting, ?) 15x37; Banks Farm 13x26(95).
Young's Birch 'Youngii' Abundant in suburban gardens. Sheffield Park (W of First Lake) **12**x**48**(94); Cedar Tree Cottage 7x45(97).
B. platyphylla Rare: collections. Wakehurst Place (Bethlehem Wood): 9x20(97).
Downy Birch *B. pubescens* Abundant and often planted, except on chalk. Park Wood, Crowhurst (streamside above railway embankment, TQ773116) 26x45(97); Linchmere Common (SU872315) 19x91@1m(97); Sheffield Park (picnic site) 14x92@0.8m(94); Hindleap Warren (roadside, TQ400328) 17x90@1m(94).
B. resinifera At Wakehurst Place (Bethlehem Wood): 13x15(97).
B. schmidtii Rare. Borde Hill (Gores Wood) 11x15(95).
Szechuan Birch *B. szechuanica* Rare. Hurst Mill (below tennis court) 17x40(97); Stanmer Park (Arboretum, p1964) 11x23(95).
B. uber At Wakehurst Place (Bethlehem Wood): 6x16(97).
Himalayan Birch *B. utilis* Occasional: large gardens. Knockbridge House 13x33+(94).
'Doorenbos' At Wakehurst Place (restaurant): 8x16(97).
'Jermyns' Becoming frequent? Wakehurst Place (Bethlehem Wood) 10x20(97).
var. *jacquemontii* Becoming common as an amenity and garden tree - thrives on chalk. Wakehurst Place (Coates Wood, hybrid?) 22x38(97).
var. *jacquemontii x B. pendula* Probably not rare. Alexandra Park (lower duckpond island) 13x45, Stanmer Park (Arboretum, p1964) 13x22(97).
var. *utilis* At Wakehurst Place (Bethlehem Wood): 9x16(97).

Silver birch

Downy birch

• **The Szechuan birch is the only form where the intense white of the bark comes off in the hand**

Paper Mulberry *Broussonetia papyrifera* At Highdown (Chalk Garden, E side): 9x24(97).

Balearic Box *Buxus balearica* Rare. Alexandra Park (Dordrecht Way, NE gate) 7x20@1.2m+(93).
Box *B. sempervirens* An uncommon native in the west; abundantly planted. Stanmer church 9x20(94); Bishop's
Palace (W garden boundary) 5x**36**@1m(97).
'Aurea Pendula' Occasional; churchyards etc. Newtimber church 4x15+(97).

BOX

Northern Incense Cedar *Calocedrus decurrens* Frequent in parks and gardens, particularly as younger tree.
Malt House (Pinetum) 35x78(97); Copthorne (small back garden) 24x110; St Roche's Arboretum (bottom
gates, fine tree) 32x87(97); Ridley's Court (top blown out) 14x99(97).

Hornbeam *Carpinus betulus* Native; abundant on heavy soils. Ashburnham: N of Sight (in grove, slender)
26x51(94), E of Reservoir Pond 16x123@1m(93); Brede (TQ825188) 14x**258**@0.5m(97).
'Fastigiata' Frequent street tree. Borde Hill (Naldred farmyard) 17x65@1.1m(95); West Dean Gardens (tennis
court) 13x79@0.9m(97).

HORNBEAMS

The Brede giant

The **hornbeam** is probably more abundant on Sussex clay than anywhere else in Britain. This is not a well-known tree, and is easily mistaken for a slightly ailing, fragile beech. Monumental it never is, but old, gnarly pollards and stubs are full of presence.

None is bigger than the tree at Brede, whose origins lie in a stem 'pleached' - cut almost through so that it can be laid horizontally - in a traditional, laid hedge. Pleaching does not kill the plant, and this tree has sent up vigorous vertical trunks along its length which have now fused to form a single mass of timber (p. 25). A big coppice by South Pond, Midhurst, has a measured diameter almost as great.

The biggest and oldest known example of the rare cut-leaved cultivar, 'Incisa', grows behind the riding school at Beauport Park - much battered and covered in moss and lichens. It was 61cm in diameter as long ago as 1908.

Cut-leaved Hornbeam 'Incisa' Rare. Beauport Park (behind riding school) 12x**111**@0.7m(97).
Blue Beech *C. caroliniana* Rare: collections. Wakehurst Place (Horsebridge Woods) 10x17(97).
C. cordata Rare: collections. Wakehurst Place (Slips) 7x23@0.3m(97).
C. laxiflora Rare: collections. Borde Hill (South Park, Borde Hill Laneside, Wilson collection) **9x32**@0.4m(95).
var. *macrostachya* Rare: collections. Nymans (Top Garden) **10x38**@0.5m(96).
C. tschonoskii At Wakehurst Place: Coates Wood 11x43, Bethlehem Wood 11x31(97).
C. turczaninowii At Highdown: Middle Garden (Farrer seed, 1914) **11x59**, and below Rose Garden (seedling of
big tree, p1937 by Queen Mary) 8x43(97).
var. *ovalifolia* At Borde Hill (Borde Hill Laneside, by South Park): 9x39@0.2m(95).

Bitternut *Carya cordiformis* Occasional; big gardens. Hollycombe: railway **29**x61, estate 21x**66**(97); Victoria
Recreation Ground (W fence) 13x41(96).
Pignut *C. glabra* Occasional: big gardens. Hollycombe (railway) **25**x46(97); Warnham Court (Wild Garden)
25x40(97); Leonardslee (below Cox's Walk) 17x40(96).
Big Shellbark Hickory *C. laciniosa* Rare: big gardens. Borde Hill: Little Bentley Wood (p1913) **23**x41, Lullings
Farm 16x**58**(95).
Red Hickory *C. ovalis* Rare. Borde Hill (Little Bentley Wood, NW) 24x35(95).
Shagbark Hickory *C. ovata* Occasional: big gardens. Hollycombe (railway) **27**x40(97); Borde Hill (Lullings
Farm) 22x51(95); Bignor Park (N lawn) 24x47(97).
Mockernut *C. tomentosa* Rare. Wakehurst Place: Bethlehem Wood **22x54**(98) and 17x49(97).

HICKORIES

American Sweet Chestnut *Castanea dentata* At Borde Hill (Warren Wood, recumbent): 6x36(96).
Sweet Chestnut *C. sativa* Abundant, except on chalk and heavy clay. Petworth Park (near Upperton)
35x226(97); Cowdray Park (towards Lodsworth) 25x364@0.4m-2m(97); Mountfield Court (gate, c1740)
18x236@0.8m(94); Herstmonceux Castle (line) 14x219(94); Buckingham Park (bowling green) 18x222(94);
Goodwood (icehouse, much died back) 9x231@0.6m(97); and see 'Big Trees'.
'Albomarginata' At Borden Wood: 19x53(97).
Cut-leaved Chestnut 'Heterophylla' At Petworth Park (House/Pleasure Grounds): 13x53(97).
Chinese Chinquapin *C. seguinii* At Borde Hill (Tolls, p1930): 18x67(95).

SWEET
CHESTNUTS

Whipped cream topping

With their stag-headed tops and bulging, corkscrew boles - the vegetable equivalent of whipped cream topping - **sweet chestnuts** manages to look ancient even when they date from the fashionable plantings of the late 18th century. If in doubt about the ages of the trees around Herstmonceux Castle, count the rings in the varnished slice through a

felled specimen which is now propped up by the tea-rooms. The biggest of all - in the far north-east corner of Cowdray Park (p. 29) - does however still give the impression of a youthful tree which will grow much bigger: it has a full, spreading dome like a thunderhead. A low branch, stouter than most mature trees, has snapped off at some distance from the trunk, but otherwise the tree has an unusually clean, flaring bole.

Castanopsis cuspidata Rare. Nymans (Wild Garden) 8x**37**+22(96).

BEAN TREES

Indian Bean *Catalpa bignonioides* Frequent - parks. Rye church 11x58@1.3m(94); Ditton Place (recumbent) x79+(96).

Hybrid Bean *C. x erubescens* Frequent - parks. Hampden Park (N of lake) 15x78(94); Chichester cathedral (E front) 13x87+(97); The Coomb 12x85; Bexhill Cemetery 13x73(94).

C. fargesii Rare: collections. Stonehurst (below house) 11x11(97); Knockbridge House 10x23(94).

Western Catalpa *C. speciosa* Rare: collections. Wakehurst Place (W of Slips) 5x37@0.5m(97).

CEDARS

Atlas Cedar *Cedrus atlantica* Frequent in large and small gardens, merging into f. *glauca*. Stanmer Park (behind House) 27x107(94); Normanhurst (caravan park) 21x154(94).

Blue Atlas Cedar f. *glauca* Abundant in suburbia. Borden Wood 30x87(97); Tilgate Park (Inn; forks) 27x**171**(96); Stansted Park (Arboretum, W side, branchy and broken) 13x**216**@0.6m(97); Ely Grange 22x159@1.8m(94); St Roche's Arboretum (S side, slender) 30x75(97).

Cyprus Cedar *C. brevifolia* Rare. Wakehurst Place (Pinetum) **23**x54(97); Cowbeech Farm 10x30(94).

Deodar *C. deodara* Abundant in large and small gardens. Leonardslee (head of Dell, splendid bole) 31x150(96); Ketches (field, good bole) 27x153(94); Stansted Park (Arboretum, NW, branchy) 27x194@0.6m(97); Worthing Crematorium (memorial lawn) 29x133(96); Newick church (very spreading) 17x139@0.8m(94).

'Aurea' Rare. Lorien 9x27(94).

'Kashmir' Rare. Lorien 9x17(94).

'Robusta' Rare. Tilgate Park (walled garden side) 14x35(96).

'Verticillata' Rare. Wakehurst Place (Pinetum) 16x43(97).

Cedar of Lebanon *C. libani* Fairly frequent, as old tree. Goodwood (cricket field, p1761) 23x289@1m, 32x292@0.5m(97); Saint Hill College 30x229@1m(96); Eridge Park (lawn) 25x223@0.6m(94); Knepp Castle (in avenue) 23x216(96); West Dean Gardens (Cedar Lawn, p1748?; taped under lopped limbs) 22x218@0.4m(97); Woolbeding House (paddock, p1761?) 26x225@0.9m(97) - and see 'Big Trees'.

'Compte de Dijon' Rare. Sheffield Park (drive) 6x37(94).

Spreading beauty

The **Cedar of Lebanon** was one of the first conifers to gain popularity as an ornamental, and it has also proved one of the most long-lived, although branches will break off in high winds.

Probably the oldest in Sussex is the tree on the Cedar Lawn at West Dean Gardens, which is thought to date from 1748. The big

Goodwood cedars, and those at West Stoke House and possibly Woolbeding House, were raised in 1761, but the tree grows fast and others of Victorian planting are almost as large.

The largest of all was planted in 1811 at Higham House, Salehurst, and blew down in 1987. This had about 30 trunks radiating from a base which, according to Alexander Howard in 1947, was 5m in diameter.

NETTLE TREES

Southern Nettle Tree *Celtis australis* Rare. Nymans (Top Garden border) 11x21(96); Borde Hill (Gorse) 9x25(95).

C. jessoensis At Borde Hill (Gorse, p1934, ?): **10x40**@1.1m(95).

C. labilis At Borde Hill (Gorse, p1934, ?): **8x37**(95).

Hackberry *C. occidentalis* Rare. Stanmer Park: Arboretum 8x16, drive 6x20(94).

C. tenuifolia At Wakehurst Place (Mansion Pond, cut back): 7x28(91).

Chinese Cow-tail Pine *Cephalotaxus fortunei* Occasional: collections. Beauport Park (caravan park) 8x22+(92).

Katsura *Cercidiphyllum japonicum* Occasional: large gardens. Duckyls Wood 20x45(96); Duckyls House (bank) 17x56++(96); Wakehurst Place (Mansion Pond) 17x103@0.3m(97).

• *The elegant katsura is instantly recognisable in autumn because of the caramel smell of the falling leaves*

Chinese Redbud *Cercis chinensis* At Nymans (Top Garden by cottage): 7x24+16+(96).

C. racemosa At Highdown (below Rose Garden): 8x**35**+(97).

Judas Tree *C. siliquastrum* Frequent: parks and small gardens. Worthing Crematorium (house site) 10x**188**@0.1m(96); Preston Park (Manor; almost horizontal) 7x49(94).

More than a bush

'Go and look at our **Judas Tree**,' the groundsmen said, when I visited Worthing Crematorium, on the A24 north of Findon. This tree (pp 2-3) grows near the site of the demolished Muntham House, by the disused drive which curves up the hill from the staff car park. Most Judas trees are bushes, noted for the rich pink flowers which bud from the trunk and branches themselves, but this is a giant. Six broken and decaying stems radiate from a solid base, rooting along their lengths and ramping for 25m beside the track.

FALSE CYPRESSES

Formosan Cypress *Chamaecyparis formosensis* Occasional; collections. Wakehurst Place (Westwood Valley) 16x51(98); Borde Hill (Warren Wood, forks, p1912) 14x**80**@1.2m(95); Tilgate Park (below walled garden, p1913) 15x38++, 15x33++ and 13x41++(96).

Lawson Cypress *C. lawsoniana* Abundant everywhere. Possingworth Park (lakeside) 30x70(94); Normanhurst (Model Farm field, divides at 2m, dying back) 23x151(94); Malt House (Pinetum, vigorous) 29x97(97).

'Allumii' Occasional as older tree. Snell Hatch Cemetery (NW) 15x41++(97).

'Aurea Smithii' Occasional? Crowborough Warren Pinetum (p1957) **14**x23+20(97).

'Aureomaculata' Rare. Barham House 17x46(94); Framfield church 9x63@0.1m(94).

f. *aureospica* Rare. Riccard's Cottage 8x25(94).

'Columnaris' Abundant (along with 'Grayswood Pillar'). Stanmer Park (Arboretum) 11m(94).

'Compacta' At Leonardslee (Below Mossy Ghyll): 10x50@0.1m(96).

'Erecta' Frequent, especially in churchyards. Borden Wood 27x115@0.8m, 26x153@0.5m(97); Buxted Park 16x117(94); Milland church (behind chapel) 25x135@0.5m(97); Sutton church 15x123@0.5m(97).

'Filifera' At Sheffield Park (N of First Lake): **11x32+**(94).

'Filiformis' Rare. Sheffield Park (Conifer Walk, p1924) 19x59(94).

'Fletcheri' Abundant in small gardens. Handcross Park (drive) 12x58@0.2m(98); Borde Hill (Gores Wood) 12x26(96); Warren House 11x29++(94).

'Fraseri' Occasional? Crowborough Warren Pinetum (p1957) 12x37(97).

'Green Spire' Occasional? Wakehurst Place (Pinetum) 6x20(97).

'Hillieri' Occasional? Borde Hill (Gores Wood) **15**x29, 13x30(96).

'Intertexta' Occasional in big gardens. St Roche's Arboretum (S slope) **30x81**(97).

'Lane' Abundant in small gardens. Crowborough Warren Pinetum (p1957) 11x34(97).

'Lutea' Frequent as older tree. Tilgate Park (Pinetum, p1905) 21x63(96).

'New Silver' Rare. Borde Hill (Gores Wood) **12x35**(96); Crowborough Warren Pinetum 11m(97).

'Oliver Slocock' At Wakehurst Place (Heath Garden): **13x53**(97).

'Pembury Blue' Occasional? Wakehurst Place (Horsebridge Woods) 8x16(97).

'Pottenii' Abundant in small gardens. Nymans (Wild Garden) **18x66**(96).

'President Roosevelt' At Wakehurst Place (Heath Garden): **13x50**(97).

'Silver Queen' Rare? Crowborough Warren Pinetum (p1957) 11x39(97).

'Smithii' Frequent? Mallydams Wood 9m(93).

'Spaeroides' At Riccard's Cottage (labelled): 7x16(94).

'Stewartii' Occasional as older tree. Tilgate Park (Pinetum, p1905) 18x32(96), Broadfield Park (wood edge W of house) 17x42(97).

'Triompf van Boskoop' Frequent in larger gardens. St Roche's Arboretum (S path, forks at 2m, ?) 29x93@1.8m(97); Tilgate Park (Pinetum, p1905) 22x58(96).

'Versicolor' Rare. Stanmer Park (Arboretum) 8x17(95).

'Wareana' At Borde Hill (Stonepit Wood): **17x41**(95).

'Westermanii' Rare. Wakehurst Place (Bethlehem Wood) 15x45(97); Crowborough Warren Pinetum (p1957) 9x29(97).

'Winston Churchill' Abundant in small gardens. Wakehurst Place (Heath Garden) 11x30++(97); West Hoathly church 10x51@0.8m+(96); Crowborough Warren Pinetum (p1957) 10x30+22(97).

'Wisselii' Occasional in larger gardens. High Beeches (p 1931) 21x77, Tilgate Park (Pinetum, p1905) 21x54(97); Handcross Park (drive) 16x68(93).

'Youngii' Rare. Hammer Lane, Linchmere (garden, ?) 19x48.

Nootka Cypress *C. nootkatensis* Occasional as old tree. St Roche's Arboretum (bottom path, leans) 29x75(97); Normanhurst (estate; layering, with the central stem nearly dead) 14x95(93); High Rocks 20x60.

'Lutea' Rare. Heaselands (N drive) 11x30(96).

'Pendula' Occasional as young tree. Warnham Court (paddock) 10x22(97).

Hinoki Cypress *C. obtusa* Frequent. Borde Hill (Warren Wood, p1916?) 23x60(95); Cowdray Park (garden by Wellingtonia avenue) 14x**85**(97).

'Aurea' Rare. Borden Wood **18**x48(97); Cowdray Park (garden pool) 17x**82**@1.2m(97).

'Aurea Nova' At Crowborough Warren Pinetum (as planted, 1957): 5x18(97).

'Crippsii' Frequent. Duckyls Wood 20x36+31(96); Tilgate Park (below walled garden, fine tree) 19x**60**(96); Sheffield Park (far S) 17x53(94); Broadfield Park 15x46+37(97).

var. *formosana* At Borde Hill (Gores Wood): 14x22(95).

'Lycopodioides' Occasional. Leonardslee (Daffodil Lawn) 19x51(96); Hollycombe (estate) 18x58(97).

'Nana Gracilis' Frequent. Sheffield Park (Conifer Walk) 7x27(94); Greyfriars 5x**49**(94); Almonry garden 6x30(94).

'Tetragona Aurea' Occasional - in small gardens. Stonehurst (valley; leans) 10x40(97).

Sawara Cypress *C. pisifera* Frequent. Borden Wood 25x59(97); Cowdray Park (garden, far N) 21x74(97); Malt House (Pinetum) 23x69(97).

'Aurea' Rare. Wakehurst Place (Westwood Valley, reverted) **23**x56(97); Crowborough Warren Pinetum (p1957) 9x37(97).

'Filifera' Occasional. Beechland 14x66(94); Alexandra Park (above herbacious beds, many layers) 14x44@1m+(93).

'Filifera Aurea' Quite frequent. Stonehurst (rockery, N) 10x29(97); Buxted Park (garden) 8x32@1.2m(94); Rutherfords Business Park (entrance) 7x31@0.9m(93).

'Plumosa' Abundant as an older tree. Cowdray Park (garden, far N) 25x90@1m(97); Fittleworth church 17x92(97); Slaugham church 19x84(96).

'Plumosa Aurea' Frequent. Midhurst cemetery 16x54(97); Ifield church 12x61(97); Battle cemetery 14x48(98); Burwash church 14x47(94).

'Squarrosa' Frequent, now replaced by 'Boulevard'. Borden Wood **26**x86@0.8m(97); Midhurst cemetery 16x81(97); St Roche's Arboretum (S of bottom glade; forks) 19x83@0.8m(97).

White Cypress *C. thyoides* Rare: collections. Nymans (bottom of Pinetum) 14x34(96); St Helens Woods (Gowers Field) 6m(97).

Chinese Fringe Tree *Chionanthus retusus* At Highdown (Middle Garden): 8x62@0.2m(97).

Yellowwood *Cladrastis lutea* Occasional; big gardens. Tilgate Park (mid S) 13x58@0.5m(96).

Chinese Yellowwood *C. sinensis* Rare. Highdown (Middle Garden, W) 7x29+(97) Stanmer Park (Arboretum, top, p1964) 7x16(94).

• *Some forms of sawara cypress, bred in old Japan, are so distinctive that European botanists once placed them in a separate genus,* Retinospora

DOGWOODS

Table Dogwood *Cornus controversa* Occasional; large gardens. Malt House (garden) 9x27(97); Stonehurst (S end of Wild Garden) 8x29+(97).
Flowering Dogwood *C. florida* Occasional; large gardens. The Hyde (lakeside) 7x16++(96).
C. kousa Frequent in large gardens. Leonardslee (below Cross Paths) 10x27(96); Tilgate Park (mid S) 8x**37**@1.1m(96).
C. macrophylla Rare. Stanmer Park (Arboretum, p1964) 7x17(94).
Cornelian Cherry *C. mas* Quite frequent in older gardens. Trotton Place 10x26++(97).
Nuttall's Cornel *C. nuttallii* Rare. Borde Hill (Pirates Adventure) 12x32(95).
Dogwood *C. sanguinea* Native; common except on poor soils. Ashcombe Bottom 9x21@0.5m +(95).
C. walteri At Wakehurst Place: Mansion Pond **15**x27, above Slips 10x**44**(97).

HAZELS

Hazel *Corylus avellana* Native; abundant. Tompset's Bank (TQ424339) 13x32++(94).
Turkish Hazel *C. colurna* Becoming frequent as an amenity tree. Wakehurst Place (by restaurant) 18x49(97).
Filbert *Corylus maxima* Occasional? Charleston Manor 7x**43**@0.9m(94).

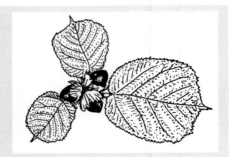

Hurdler's delight

The **hazel** is one of the most abundant and cosmopolitan of understorey trees, and one of the most appreciated by traditional foresters. Its whippy young stems provide the material for hurdle-making and the binders or hethering used in hedgelaying; older growths make smooth, straight stakes.

With its leaves like pale yellow moons in December, and its yellow, lambstail catkins, a hazel brightens the winter woods; it burns brightly with a smell of caramel. It is rare to find a hazel trunk which has been left to grow to its full age.

The tree by Tompset's Bank in Forest Row (on the right going up) is much the biggest I have seen: it has an explosion of writhing trunks the size of anacondas, and a crown like a spreading oak (p. 44).

Himalayan Tree Cotoneaster *Cotoneaster frigidus* Occasional. Hollycombe (railway) 13x28++(97); Alexandra Park (behind war memorial) 10x36++(93); Worthing Crematorium (SW) 9x76@0.1m(96).
C. frigidus x henryana At Wakehurst Place (S of Westwood Valley): 8x32(97).

THORNS

Crataegus chrysocarpa Occasional? (these trees unconfirmed). Borde Hill (Stonepit Wood, died back) 11x27@0.8m(95).
Cockspur Thorn *C. crus-galli* Occasional. Nymans (North Park) **8**x27(96); St Roche's Arboretum (bottom entrance) 6x**37**(97). An attractive related species at Alexandra Park (Dordrecht Way, SW gate): **8**x**58**@1.2m(93).
C. x dippeleana At Borde Hill (Warren Wood W gate): 6x21(96).
C. ellwangeriana Rare? Goldsmith's Avenue street planting, Crowborough 6x21(94); Brackley 5x30.
C. x grignonensis Occasional amenity tree. Alexandra Park (Thorpe's Wood, p1935) 9x29(93); Wakehurst Place (Westwood Lake) 8x24(97).
C. henryi At Borde Hill (below lake dam, hung up, p1941): 5x35@0.4m(95).
Oriental Thorn *C. laciniata* Occasional. Lorien 9m(94); Nymans (North Park) 8x32(96); Bexhill Cemetery 6x23(94).
Hybrid Cockspur Thorn *C. x lavallei* Frequent street tree. Greenway, Horsham 9x40(98); Buxted Park (footpath outside Hotel) 9x35(94); Groombridge village hall 6x32(94).
Scarlet Haw *C.* "mollis" Occasional - a series of species only separable in flower. Warnham Court 8x36@1m(97).
Hawthorn *C. monogyna* Native; abundant everywhere. Beauport Park (Hollow Wood) **15**x33+(92); Chichester Canal (between Cutfield and Dudley bridges, S embankment) 8x62(97); Warnham Court (Nursery House) 9x57(97); Hotham Park (N side) 14x31(97).

The ubiquitous thorn

With its enthusiasm for invading chalk grasslands, its tolerance of dense shade, and its unbeatable prickly presence in hedgerows, the **hawthorn** is probably the commonest tree in Sussex.

In fact there are two, very similar species: the Midland thorn - restricted to ancient woods and hedges on stiff clay - tends to have darker haws and its less-lobed leaves are generally a darker, glossier green, so that it sometimes almost recalls a holly-bush. Wild trees with pinkish blossom are likely to be Midland thorn, or hybrids.

In the wild, too, the Midland never seems to reach the substantial sizes of its common cousin, though the ubiquitous garden form, 'Paul's Scarlet', is vigorous enough. By the Sydney Road roundabout in Haywards Heath (TQ336247) there is a wild bush with double white pompom flowers.

What may have been the oldest and biggest thorn in Sussex, however, was neither of these species, but one of the American scarlet haws, growing in Eastergate churchyard until its removal in 1998: 8x99@0.1m(97). Several hundred American thorn species have been described, and many of them introduced to Britain, so identification is perilous: this one was probably *C. chrysocarpa*, and had several trunks radiating from a hollow centre.

Glastonbury Thorn 'Biflora' Rare. Stanmer Park (Arboretum, bottom, p1964) 5x17(95).
'Multiplex' At Stanmer Park (Arboretum, bottom, p1964): 6x27(95).
'Stricta' Quite frequent in streets. Three Bridges Playing Field 9x27(98).

Pink May *C. oxycantha* 'Paul's Scarlet' Abundant. Rye church 9x**48**(94).
'Plena' Rare. Preston Park, Preston Road edge (one of three): 7x38@1.1m(94).
'Punicea Flore Plena' Occasional. Winchelsea church 9x**43**@1.3m, 8x**51**(94).
C. pentagyna At Alexandra Park (over stream from hard tennis courts, dying back): **7**x**37**(93).
C. persistens Rare. Banks Farm 5x17(95).
C. pinnatifida Rare. Warnham Court (Nursery House) 8x22(97).
Broad-leaved Cockspur Thorn *C. prunifolia* Frequent; streets and parks. St Julian's church, Southwick 9x34(94); Selsfield Drive, Moulsecoomb 8x33(95).
C. punctata 'Brevispina' At Borde Hill (Pinetum gate): 6x27@1.2m(95).
Tansy-leaved Thorn *C. tanacetifolia* Rare. Warnham Court (Wild Garden) **10**x31 and 8x**48**(97).
C. tomentosa Rare. Arlington church **7**x**37**(94); Temple Grove School 5x37(94).

X Crataemespilus grandiflora Rare. Preston Park (side by clock-tower) 7x34(94).

Japanese Red Cedar *Cryptomeria japonica* Frequent. Leonardslee (above Cox's Walk) 31x99(96) Beauport Park (Babylon Wood, var. *sinensis*) 26x129(93).
'Compacta' Rare. Dangstein **15**x**53**(97).
'Cristata' Rare. West Dean Gardens (Spring Garden) 13x31(97).
'Elegans' Frequent in small gardens. Pashley Manor (SE side) 19x65(94); Beauport Park (Oak Wood, a forest of stems spreading over 30m) 14x87++(92); Wakehurst Place (Pinetum) 18x68(97).
'Lobbii' Occasional. Hollycombe (gardens) 29x79(97); Normanhurst (caravan park drive, massive tree with a ring of low limbs) 28x142@1.8m/x194@1m(93).
'Lycopodioides' At Wakehurst Place (Heath Garden): 8x31(97).

Cunninghamia konishii At Borde Hill (Gores Wood, p1940?): **12**x**31**(95).
Chinese Coffin Tree *C. lanceolata* Occasional; many bigger gardens. Malt House (path to Pinetum) 22x49(97); Sheffield Park House 19x83(94); Beechland 15x80(94); Holmbush 14x82(96).

Golden Leyland Cypress *X Cupressocyparis leylandii* 'Castlewellan Gold' Abundant in suburbia. Wakehurst Place (Slips) **15**x**50**(97).
Leyland Cypress 'Haggerston Grey' Commonest garden tree. Wakehurst Place (above Pinetum) 32x83(97).
'Leighton Green' Occasional? Pickwell (line in woods) 21x49(96); Wakehurst Place (Entrance Grounds) 18x100@1m(97).
'Naylor's Blue' Rare? Wakehurst Place (Slips, p1969) 21x**60**(98)).
'Stapehill 20' At Cedar Tree Cottage: 12x55(97).
X C. notabilis In several collections. Borde Hill (Gores Wood) 13x28(96); Wakehurst Place (Slips) 12x**41**(97).
X C. ovensii At Wakehurst Place (Pinetum): **16**x**36**(97).

Arizona Cypress *Cupressus arizonica* Occasional. Bishop's Palace (?) 10x36+(97).
Mourning Cypress *C. funebris* At Nymans (Garden Cottage, dense young tree): 11x35(96).
Smooth Arizona Cypress *C. glabra* Now frequent in small gardens, generally as 'Pyramidalis'. Little Glebe 16x36(97); The Sheep House 13x57@0.9m(94); Alexandra Park (below Pets Corner) 15x55@1.2m(93); Memorial Gardens, Crawley 12x50@1m(97).
'Conica' At Stanmer Park (Arboretum, p1964): 16x32(94).
Cedar of Goa *C. lusitanica* Occasional; sometimes in small gardens. Borde Hill (Stonepit Wood) 28x77(95); Wakehurst Place (SE of Mansion Pond) 21x83@1m(97); Crowborough Warren Pinetum 13x59(97).
'Glauca' Rare. Borde Hill (Warren Wood) 13x27(95); Leonardslee (Coronation Garden) 9x32(96); Snell Hatch Cemetery (middle avenue) 10x51@0.1m(97).
'Glauca Pendula' At Stonehurst (Wild Garden, S): 10x36(97).
Monterey Cypress *C. macrocarpa* Abundant near coasts. Beauport Park: by 10th, 27x154, behind 13th tee, 17x325@0.2-1m(97); Crimsham Manor 15x275@1-1.5m(97); Westfield Place (garden of Pinewood) 21x210@0.9m(94); Birdham church (gnarled old tree) 11x137(97); and see 'Big Trees'.
'Donard Gold' Occasional? Sedgewick Park 16x69@0.6m(97); Wakehurst Place (Pinetum) 15x57@1.2m(97); Leonardslee (below Camellia Walk) 16x35(96); Alexandra Park (lawn below Buckshole, p1973) 12x43(93).
'Fastigiata' Occasional. Rusper (fieldside) 24x81(97); Borde Hill (South Lodge) 24x50.
'Goldcrest' And similar clones, abundant in suburbia. Stonehurst (path to Wild Garden) 14x39(97).
'Lutea' Frequent as older tree. Barham House 20x146@0.2m(94); Clock House 17x107(93).

- *The* Crataemespilus *is a rare example of a hybrid between two quite different trees, medlar and Midland thorn. It is picturesque and has large white flowers, but remains very rare*

Leyland Cypress

TRUE CYPRESSES

Outdoing California

The **Monterey Cypress** grows much bigger at Beauport Park than it does in its native clifftops on the Monterey Peninsula of California.

Several trees - probably from the first introduction into Britain - were planted at Beauport around 1843, one of them on top of the buried but perfectly-preserved Roman road from the iron-works to the nearest port (at Sedlescombe). This has become the biggest of all, squatting like a lignified octopus in the derelict woodland, with all its great limbs resting on the ground. Its head was blown out in 1987 but it remains a bright, healthy green and is still growing furiously - which is curious, as Monterey cypresses in urban gardens begin to die, from the top down, when they are much younger and a tiny fraction of this size.

Elwes and Henry told of a fox raising its cubs at head-height within the cavernous branches of one of the Beauport trees.

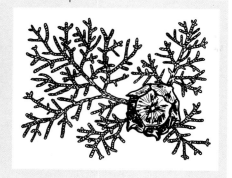

TRUE CYPRESSES

Nevada Cypress *C. nevadensis* Rare recent introduction. Nymans (top of Pinetum) 8x24(97).
C. sargentii At Wakehurst Place (Pinetum): **11x36**(97).
Italian Cypress *C. sempervirens* Frequent; in many small gardens and churchyards. Borde Hill (Warren Wood, exceedingly slender) 23x28(95); Kidbrooke Park 13x46(94); Staplefield church (spreading form) 8x59@ground(96); Bexhill Cemetery 17x42(94); Rusper church 14x25++(97); Woodmancote church 12x25++(97).
Bhutan Cypress *C. torulosa* Rare: collections. Wakehurst Place (Heath Garden) 13x40(97).
var. *corneyana* At Borde Hill (drive by Gores Wood): 7x19(95).

Daphniphyllum macropodum At Hollycombe (gardens): 6x27@0.9m(97).

Dove Tree *Davidia involucrata* Rare as the type: Borde Hill (Stonepit Wood, ?) 19x31(95); Wakehurst Place (Slips) 13x44++(97).
var. *vilmoriniana* Quite frequent in bigger gardens. Legsheath Farm 16x46++(94); Wakehurst Place (head of Westwood Valley, cut back) 8x61(97); St Roche's Arboretum (bottom glade) 16x40(97); Duckyls Wood 16x42(96); Gravetye Manor (East Garden) 10x57(97).

Date-Plum *Diospyros lotus* Occasional in large gardens. Nymans (Wild Garden) 15x25(96); Wakehurst Place (head of Westwood Valley) 14x34(97); Stansted Park (Arboretum) 8x33@1m(97); Highdown (Chalk Garden, E side, p1912) 9x28(97).

Discaria discolor At Borde Hill (Bride's Pool): 5x52@0.3m(97).

Chilean Firebush *Embothrium coccineum* 'Norquinco Valley'. Occasional in larger gardens. High Beeches (Loderi Walk) 12x12++(97); Lorien 6x18(94).

Emmenopterys henryi Rare. Wakehurst Place (Slips: first specimen to flower in Britain) 9x23++(97); Borde Hill (Azalea Ring, p1928) 8x30(95).

Loquat *Eriobotrya japonica* Occasional. Bishop's Palace (second stem cut) 5x21(97).

GUM TREES

• *There are more than 500 species of gum tree in Australia. Only a handful, adapted to the high mountains, are hardy in Sussex*

Black Gum *Eucalyptus aggregata* Rare. Herstmonceux Castle (E of moat) 17x**89**@0.8m and 13x**79**(94).
Alpine Cider Gum *E. archeri* Rare. Malt House (garden) 10x17(97); Cookscroft 7x19(97).
E. caesia At Architectural Plants (only one in Britain?): 12x34(96).
E. crenulata At Cookscroft: 9x19(97).
Tasmanian Snow Gum *E. coccifera* Rare. Lorien 17x32(94).
Mountain Gum *E. dalrympleana* Frequent as young garden tree. Petworth Park (N end of Pleasure Grounds) 20x70+59(97).
Tingiringi Gum *E. glaucescens* Rare. Architectural Plants 11x17(96); Cookscroft 10x23(97).
Blue Gum *E. globulus* Occasionally planted but not fully hardy. Middleton-on-Sea (small garden) 8x17.
Cider Gum *E. gunnii* Abundant in suburbia. Selehurst 33x113(93); Staplefield Place (Wilderness) 25x153(96).
Whittingehame Gum 'Whittingehamensis' Frequent. Sheffield Park House (p1912) 22x**148**(94); Little Glebe 20x81(97).
Yellow Gum *E. johnstonii* At Cookscroft: 9x17(97).
Shining Gum *E. nitens* A lovely tree at Cookscroft: 11x28(97).
Smithton Peppermint *E. nitida* Rare. Fair Oak (?) 16x32(97).
Small-leaved Gum *E. parvifolia* Occasional. Architectural Plants 12x35@1m(96); Sheffield Park (Reservoir Pond, regrowth from tree blown 1959) 10x30++(94).
Jounama Snow Gum *E. pauciflora* subsp. *debeuzevillei* Rare. Alexandra Park (between hard tennis courts) **12x33**(93).
Snow Gum *E. pauciflora* subsp. *niphophila* Frequent as young garden tree. Lorien 14x23(94); Wakehurst Place (above Slips) 10x39(97).
Spinning Gum *E. perriniana* Quite frequent in small gardens. Ansty (front garden) 15x30(96); Architectural Plants 12x35@1m(96).
Alpine Yellow Gum *E. subcrenulata* Rare. Wakehurst Place (Coates Wood) 11x19(97).
Urn Gum *E. urnigera* Rare. Cookscroft 11x18+16(97).

Gutta-Percha Tree *Eucommia ulmoides* Rare. Brook House 6x25++(97).

Ulmo *Eucryphia cordifolia* Occasional: large gardens. Borde Hill (Gores Wood memorial) 6x21++(96).
E. glutinosa Occasional; large gardens. Nymans (Walled Garden) 9x22+21+(96); South Lodge Hotel (rockery) 7x23++(96).
E. x intermedia Occasional: large gardens. Borde Hill (Gores Wood, p1937?)15x26+(95); St Helens Woods (barbecue) 9x13@1.2m(93).
E. x nymansensis 'Nymansay' Frequent in big and some small gardens. Borde Hill (Gores Wood) 18x30+29+(95); Nymans (W of Walled Garden) 14x34(96).

Spindle *Euonymus europaeus* Native; frequent, except on light soils. South Lodge Hotel (rockery; appears to be the wild species) 5x27@1m(96).
E. phellomanus At Highdown (Lower Garden): 6x36@0.2m(97).

Japanese Beech *Fagus crenata* Rare. Borde Hill (Peartree Wood) 17x56(95).
Chinese Beech *F. engleriana* Occasional: collections. Borde Hill (Lullings Ghyll, p1928) 15x**52**(95); Stanmer Park (Great Wood above Arboretum) 10x20(95).
American Beech *F. grandifolia* At Wakehurst Place (Bethlehem Wood): 11x31(97).
Oriental Beech *F. orientalis* Occasional. Wakehurst Place: Slips **28x150**(98), Coates Wood 22x107@0.5(97); Petworth Park (lawn N of House, biggest of six around Park) 22x**97**(97); Borde Hill (Peartree Wood) 19x69(95); Leonardslee (Cox's Walk) 17x61(96).
Beech *F. sylvatica* Native; abundant except on heavy clay. Coomb Wood 39x140(95); Eridge Park: by footpath out of Frant village (TQ587351) 26x**284**@1.1m, Mill Wood 34x206(94); Cowdray Park (Golf Course by Oaters Wood, much decayed) 20x230(97); Pestalozzi Children's Village (Gilly Wood) 25x210(93); Ashburnham: park near road at Steven's Crouch (long, buttressed bole, decaying) 28x232(98), drive (splendid tree with 8m bole) 32x198(93); Stanmer Park (monument) 33x183(94); High Hurstwood, Mountfield (very fine) 32x195(94); Hindleap Warren ("Witches' Tree", gnarled old pollard) 28x199@0.8m; and see 'Big Trees'.

At the mercy of the wind

When I was exploring the hilly, central region of the High Weald in 1994, one of the chief excitements was to stumble upon first the largest **beech** tree in Britain, then the second largest, then the third, and then the fourth largest.

Historically, grander trees have been known, but beeches are shortlived among large-growing trees and, at present, this Sussex quartet has no competition. The largest and the most shapely of all grows on the footpath into Eridge Park from Frant village, and is magnificently situated where the steep wood suddenly opens out to give a vista of the old Park. It is a pollard, with a fluted bole and a great platform of roots, and is unlikely to be less than 400 years old.

The only historic measurement known is from 1956, when Alan Mitchell discovered it because, like me, he was walking the 5km from the Eridge Park pinetum to Frant station. Often, champion trees do not allow a sense of their true stature when first glimpsed, because they are so perfectly proportioned. In my first view of the Frant beech, however, it was given scale by a family picnicking beneath it, and this was enough to hasten me, scratched and weary, up the long slope from the Park (p. 22).

The two closest rivals to this tree - neither so perfectly shaped - stand in other, private parts of Eridge Park. The next biggest is in Broadstone Warren - an ancient woodland on Ashdown Forest - a little to the left of the path from the Wych Cross Visitor Centre down into Forest Row. Growing amid dark pines on the sunless side of the hill, it is as sinister and knobbly and black with algae as the tree at Frant is friendly, symmetrical and bleached with sun and wind. Many other big, pollard beeches stand in hedgerows and copses all around the High Weald.

The tallest native tree in Sussex, by my measurements, is another beech growing not far away at Coomb Wood. Its roots are in the stream which flows in a steep ravine through the wood and joins the Medway at Hartfield, and it owes its height to this situation, as there are no other notably tall trees in the wood. The best of the Slindon beeches, which all blew down in 1987, were slightly taller, as were trees lost in Burrage Wood at Ashburnham Place and in Great Wood at Stanmer Park.

It is easier to associate the beech with the giant conifers we can grow than with other native trees: clean-bole, dark-leaved, and towering up out of the poorest of soils, it dominates the landscape rather than settling into it, and suffers horribly from windthrow and from polluted urban air.

The night of the 16th October 1987 ruined nearly all the county's best beechwoods, and perhaps the best example left is on the upper slopes of the Mens around Bedham. This is like the interior of a cathedral, awesome and silent, lit by shafts of sun; a place for creatures to congregate in, perhaps, rather than to live. It will take centuries for all the losses to be made good: beech is slow to establish, especially on chalk where there is sycamore to compete with it, and it only grows its characteristically long, grey boles when side-shelter already exists.

Charles Goring, establishing Chanctonbury Ring in 1760, carried bottles of water up the hill for his trees in dry weather: perhaps the climate has become windier since those days. In 1794, Robert Marsham wrote to Gilbert White about the magnificent beeches of Herstmonceux Castle, which is situated on the edge of the Pevensey Levels in an area too windswept now to grow trees of height. One beech felled here around 1750 had run 25m to the first branch.

The practice of carving initials into the bark of beeches is nothing new. In 1947, a big tree at Beauport, which collapsed around 1975, still had legible dates on it going back to 1812.

The Dawyck beech, with its perm of vertical branches, is now a favourite tree with local authorities; probably the first even municipal planting was at Thorpe's Wood in Alexandra Park in 1935. A wild sport, almost as fastigiate as the Dawyck seedling, grows on a ridge in Cuckfield Park (TQ292249) and is a conspicuous tree of 23x92(96).

'Albovariegata' Rare. Alexandra Park (beech collection, mainly reverted) 22x32(93); Nymans (North Park) 18x50(96).
Fern-leaved Beech 'Aspleniifolia' Occasional. Beauport Park (opposite 10th tee) 22x122(97); Highbrook House (roadside) 19x115(97); Nymans (house drive) 21x101(96); Alexandra Park (beech collection) 22x55(93).
f. *cuprea* An occasional 'sport'. Stanmer Park (Arboretum) 14x35(94).
Dawyck Beech 'Dawyck' Quite frequent. Wakehurst Place (Horsebridge Woods, by Bloomers Valley) 25x40(97); Alexandra Park (Thorpe's Wood, p1935) 15x66@1.2m(93); Nymans (Walled Garden/road) 24x57 and 22x57(96); Warnham Court (Wild Garden) 22x62(97); Hotham Park 18x50(97).
Oak-leaved Beech 'Laciniata' Rare. Alexandra Park (beech collection) 22x95(93).
'Latifolia' Rare. Alexandra Park (beech collection, cut back) 12x85(93).
'Luteovariegata' Rare. Buxted Park (garden) 25x**107**(91).
Weeping Beech 'Pendula' Occasional. Holmbush 21x102(96); Thorne Lodge (a shapely form, less weeping than most, which produces weeping seedlings) 13x127(94); Worthing Crematorium 17x73(96); Hills Cemetery 11x73(97); Hotham Park 20x63(97) Horsham Sainsbury's (Blackhorse Way gate) 15x95(98).

BEECHES

'Prince George of Crete' At Borde Hill (llama paddock): **16x67**(95).
Copper Beech *f. purpurea* Abundant (avenue of some 400 trees at Telegraph House). Hollybridge Wood 31x121(94); Pestalozzi Children's Village (east park) 21x162(93).
'Purpurea Latifolia' Rare? Sedgewick Park 17x82(97).
'Purpurea Pendula' Occasional as young tree. Cedar Tree Cottage (p1938) 3x30(97).
'Rotundifolia' Rare. West Dean Gardens (college front) 14x53(97); Highdown (Lower Garden) 12x65(97).
'Tricolor' Rare. Leonardslee (Cox's Walk) 19x64(93); Nymans (North Park) 17x57(96).
Golden Beech 'Zlatia' Occasional. Nymans (North Park, p1912) 24x87(96).

Fig *Ficus carica* Frequent and naturalised near coasts. West Wittering church 6x27@1m(97).

Patagonian Cypress *Fitzroya cupressoides* Occasional: large gardens. High Beeches (Glade) 12x41@1m(97); Leonardslee (head of Mossy Ghyll) 12x38+22(96).

ASHES

White Ash *Fraxinus americana* Occasional. Tilgate Park (towards zoo) 21x42(96); Borde Hill (N of Tolls) 15x73(95).
Narrow-leaved Ash *F. angustifolia* Occasional; some street trees. Borde Hill (Lullings Farm, 'Lentiscifolia') 21x61(95); Beauport Park (Hollow Wood) 14x92(97).
'Australis' At Borde Hill (Little Bentley Wood): 11x43(95).
'Raywood' Now frequent as amenity planting. Stanmer Park (Arboretum, p1964) 16x20(95); Woodvale Crematorium (chapel) 14x43(94); Bexhill Down (Leisure Centre corner) 12x29(94).
'Veltheimii' At Borde Hill (by Gorse): 18x62@2.2m(95).
Chinese Manna Ash *F. chinensis* var. *rhyncophylla* At Stanmer Park (Arboretum, p1964): **15x27**(94).
Ash *F. excelsior* Abundant except on sand. St Roche's Arboretum (mid/N) 36x120; Haremere Hall (field near river, low pollard) 24x240@1m(95); Cowdray Park (behind ruins) 21x192@1m(97); Borders (by stile; buttressed bole) 22x172(94); Morebread Farmyard (pollard) 29x172(94); Balcombe (behind scout hut) 32x143(96); Offham (path above river towards Lewes) 32x132@1.1m(94); Waldron church 20x150@0.6m(94).

Complex characters

The **ash** has at least three quite different personalities.

Sometimes is is the coarse, pushy coloniser of ungrazed downs. Sometimes it is the shapely, daintily-foliaged timber tree of woods on rich soil: such trees are never long-lived, and the ash at Winchelsea under which John Wesley preached his last sermon in October 1790 has long been replaced.

Sometimes, however, ashes become the immemorial, gnarled and mossy coppice stools of ancient woodlands. The huge tree by the Rother below Haremere Hall is a low-cut pollard on a hedge-bank, probably of no great age. Perhaps the oddest ash (ashes?) in Sussex is at Ashburnham, close to the gate into the field behind the Broad Water temple (p. 7). Two slender trunks arise, with sky between them, and then, at head-height, fuse to make a single, balanced tree.

'Aurea' at Borde Hill (by Great Bentley Wood, p1913): 7x23(95).
Single-leaved Ash 'Diversifolia' Occasional. Borde Hill (Lullings Ghyll) 17x42(95); Wakehurst Place (back drive) 16x63(97); Herstmonceux Castle (woods to NE, much died back) 16x44(94); Hotham Park (died back) 11x50(97).
Golden Ash 'Jaspidea' Becoming a frequent amenity tree. High Beeches (New Bridge, p1914) 14x62(97).
Weeping Ash 'Pendula' Quite frequent. Normanhurst (below caravan park) 17x85(93); Motcombe Gardens (hollow) 14x90(94); Cedar Tree Cottage 16x85(97); Moat Lane Chapel, Chichester 11x83(97); Chiddingly church 13x70(94).
Oregon Ash *F. latifolia* Rare. Fontridge Manor 13x39(94).
Black Ash *F. nigra* At Borde Hill (beyond Stephanie's Glade): **17x33**(95).
Manna Ash *F. ornus* Frequent street tree. Haremere Hall (behind house, 'Magic Tree') 23x107(94); Beauport Park (caravan park, pollarded) x103(92); Hills Cemetery, Horsham 17x100(97).
Red Ash *F. pennsylvanica* Occasional: mostly big gardens. Borde Hill (North Park) 23x63(95); Stanmer Park (Arboretum, p1964) 18x34(94); Arundel Castle (behind church, with tiny deformed leaves) 10x28(97).
F. spaethiana Rare: collections. Stanmer Park (Arboretum, p1964) 10x15(94); Borde Hill (S of Little Bentley Wood) 6x32@1.2m(96).
Green Ash *F. subinteggerima* Occasional; municipal plantings especially in Hastings. Forest Row (back of recreation ground next to Forester's Arms, taped over torn limb) 16x**61**(94); Borde Hill (dam of lake) 13x49(95); Oaklands Park, Chichester (W side) 12x48(97); Amberley First School 12x36(97).
Arizona Ash *F. velutina* Rare: collections. Borde Hill (by Gorse) 13x**37**(95).

Mount Etna Broom *Genista aetnensis* Occasional. Offington Avenue, Worthing (front garden) 8x40@1m.

• *The ginkgo is one of the world's most primitive trees. Its popularity in gardens means that it has now returned to Sussex after an exile of 150 million years*

Maidenhair Tree *Ginkgo biloba* Frequent. Leonardslee (below Loderi Garden) 22x50(96); Clapham House (fine bole) 20x103(94); Ham Manor (clubhouse, forks) 19x119@0.5m(96); Alexandra Park (rose garden; female; taped over limb scar) 16x102(93); Knight's Gate (good bole) 21x88(94).
'Fastigiata' Occasional. Cumberland House **19x78**@0.5m, 17x46(97).

Chinese Locust *Gleditsia sinensis* Rare. Borde Hill (Garden of Allah) 6x33(95).
Honey Locust *G. triacanthos* Occasional: several small gardens. Borde Hill (North Park) 19x51(95).
'Sunburst' Occasional. Coates Manor (original British introduction) **12x41**(97).

Chinese Swamp Cypress *Glyptostrobus lineatus* At Nymans (Top Garden, 100-year-old tree): 5x13(96).

Griselinia littoralis Occasional near coasts. Knockbridge House 7x26@1.3m ++(94); South Lodge Hotel (rockery) 6x60+46(96).

Kentucky Coffee Tree *Gymnocladus dioicus* Occasional. Banks Farm 7x15(94); Alexandra Park (stream by boating lake) 5x19(93).

Hakea lissosperma At Borde Hill (Gores Wood): 8x20(96).

Snowdrop Tree *Halesia carolina* Occasional; larger gardens. Leonardslee (beyond Camellia Walk) 9x20(96); Horsted Place Hotel 8x42(94).
H. monticola Occasional (difficult to differentiate from *carolina*). Tilgate Forest Lodge 12x29+28+(96); Mountfield Court (path to Temple Wood) 7x55(94).

Idesia polycarpa Rare. Stanmer Park (nursery borders, dying back) 8x29(94).

Ilex x *altaclarensis* 'Golden King' Occasional. Tilgate Park (below walled garden) 8x19+18(96); Battle Abbey (near Harold's stone) 4x25@1m(98).
Highclere Holly 'Hodginsii' Occasional in old parks. Alexandra Park (Bohemia gates) 15x45++(94); Blakers Park 9x82@0.2m(94).
'Lawsoniana' Occasional. Wakehurst Place (Slips) 9x13++(97); Legsheath Farm 6x20(94).
'Wilsonii' Rare. Borde Hill: Gores Wood 11x21(95), Pirates Adventure 9x26(95).
Holly *I. aquifolium* Native; abundant everywhere. Borden Wood 20x74@0.3m(97); Trotton (downriver from Bridge, E bank) 8x70+(97); Leonardslee (top of bank beyond Camellia Walk) 10x97@0.2m(96); Beanacre 15x76@?(93); East Preston church 8x82@0.3m(97).
'Argentea Longifolia' At Nymans (behind Old Tennis Lawn): 10x29(96).
f. *argenteomarginata* Frequent in small gardens. Buxted Park (garden) 17x31(94); Handcross Park (woods) 10x37(98); Alexandra Park (by Burnside) 11x36(93).
Perry's Weeping Holly 'Argenteomarginata Pendula' Occasional. Milton Mount Gardens 5x23(97); West Dean House (West Lawn) 3x33@1m(97).
'Aurea Angustifolia' Rare. Buxted Park (garden, ?) 11x**55**(94).
'Aurifodina' At Nymans (Laurel Walk): 6x16(96).
'Ciliata Major' At Handcross Park (woods,?) 9x41@0.8m(98).
'Crispa' Rare. Handcross Park (woods) 11x37(98); Wildpark, Moulsecoomb (NE side) 9x23(94).
Hedgehog Holly 'Ferox' Rare. Alexandra Park (Holly Walk) **11**x23(93).
Silver Hedgehog Holly 'Ferox Argentea' Occasional in small gardens. Fair Oak 12x36(97); Manor of Dean 8x26(97).
'Golden Queen' Frequent. Whiligh 11x30(94); Ashdown Park Hotel 9x37(94); Corseley Rd, Groombridge 10x34(94).
'Handsworth New Silver' Frequent in small gardens. Walberton church 11x**46**(97).
'Laurifolia Aurea' At Alexandra Park (Holly Walk, ?) 10x23(93).
Weeping Holly 'Pendula' Occasional. South Hartfield House 7x37(94); Dangstein 6x**49**@0.3m(97).
'Pyramidalis' Occasional in small gardens. Alexandra Park (Dordrecht Way, W side mid) **14**x41(93).
'Silver Queen' Occasional. Mountfield Court 8x32(94); Wivelsfield church 8x27(94).
Japanese Holly *I. crenata* f. *latifolia* At Alexandra Park (Holly Walk): 8m(93).
Himayalan Holly *I. dipyrena* Rare: collections. Leonardslee (above Cox's Walk) **14**x51(96); Borde Hill (Pirates Adventure, p1929) 12x41(95).
I. fargesii At Borde Hill (Gores Wood): 8x20+16(95).
Tarajo *I. latifolia* Rare. High Beeches (Magnolia Garden) 8x25+21+(94).
I. pedunculosa At Borde Hill (Pirates Adventure): **11x28**(95).
I. pernyi var. *veitchii* Occasional: large gardens. Wakehurst Place (Westwood Valley) 11x**22**+(97).

Japanese Walnut *Juglans ailantifolia* Rare. Highlands 14x45(87); Leonardslee (wallaby pen) 10x51(96).
Chinese Walnut *J. cathayensis* At Borde Hill (Little Bentley Wood, dying back, p1911): 12x26(95).
Butternut *J. cinerea* Rare. Newick Park 13x27++, 12x31++(94).
Manchurian Walnut *J. mandshurica* Rare. Firle Place (park in front of house) 11x69(94).
Black Walnut *J. nigra* Frequent amenity tree. Heathfield Park House 25x112(94); Ashburnham (West Garden, taped over cut limb) 17x124(93); Gravetye Forest (lakeside, slender) 25x53(97); Seaford College 22x123(97).
Walnut *J. regia* Frequent in small gardens. Watergate House 21x50; Combe Manor 15x119(94); Manor of Dean 14x119(97).

• *Honey locusts are notable for the vicious triple spines in the bark. Tree-measurers beware!*

HOLLIES

• *The hedgehog holly has spines across the leaves as well as round the edges. It has been grown in gardens since Stuart times*

WALNUTS

JUNIPERS

Chinese Juniper *Juniperus chinensis* Occasional, mainly in churchyards. Nuthurst church 15x67@0.2m(96); Staplefield church ('Kaizuka'?) 9x65@1m(96); Rogate church 13x48(97).
'Aurea' Occasional. Sheffield Park (N of Second Lake) 11x36(94); Nymans (bottom of Pinetum) 11x28++(96).
'Keteleerii' At Dangstein: 10x30(97).
var. *shepperdii* At Stanmer Park (Arboretum, p1964): 7x15(95).
'Variegata' At Lodsworth church: 6x17(97).
Syrian Juniper *J. drupacea* At Borde Hill (Gores Wood): 6x17(96).
Grecian Juniper *J. excelsa* At Borde Hill (Warren Wood): 11x15(95).
J. indica At Wakehurst Place (Pinetum): **11x18**++(97).
Cox's Juniper *J. recurva* var. *coxii* Occasional; well-planted gardens. Sheffield Park (cascade, p1925) 12x25(94).
Temple Juniper *J. rigida* Rare: collections. Borde Hill (Warren Wood) 14x32(95).
Meyer's Juniper *J. squamata* 'Meyeri' Abundant in small gardens. Alexandra Park (below pumping station) 8x20@1.2m(93).
Pencil Cedar *J. virginiana* Occasional as an old tree. Borden Wood 17x28(97); Beauport Park (behind Hotel) 15x64@1.2m(92); Coldwaltham church 10x47(97).
'Canaertii' At Riccard's Cottage: 8x23@0.9m(94).
'Glauca' Occasional; large gardens. Borde Hill (Gores Wood) **13x30**(95); Chiddinglye 10x26(96).

• *Pencil cedar provides the traditional wood for pencils. The sour smell is characteristic of many junipers*

Castor Oil Tree *Kalopanax pictus* Rare. Brickwall (Arboretum) 11x25(94); High Beeches (path from entrance, p1974) 10x31(97).
var. *maximowiczii* Occasional. Wakehurst Place (Entrance Grounds) 12x39@1m(97); Nymans (Pergola) 10x63(96).

Keteleeria davidiana Rare: collections. Wakehurst Place (Pinetum) **11**x26(97).

Golden Rain Tree *Koelreuteria paniculata* Occasional: parks and larger gardens. Gildredge Park (Manor Garden) 11x40(94); Worthing Crematorium (SW) 11x29@1.2m(96).

LABURNUMS

Scots Laburnum *Laburnum alpinum* Rare? The Hyde 10x60(96).
Laburnum *L. anagyroides* Abundant. Singleton cemetery (leans, decaying) 6x53@0.5m(97).
Voss' Laburnum *L. x watereri* Abundant. Alexandra Park (Thorpe's Wood, now hollow, p1935) 9x44@1.2m(93); Hurstpierpoint church 7x51(97).

LARCHES

Common Larch *Larix decidua* Abundant as an older tree. Leonardslee (Cross Paths) 35x76(96); St Roche's Arboretum (centre S) 30x116(97).
Dunkeld Larch *L. x eurolepis* Abundant - mostly plantations. Ashburnham: N of Sight 30x75, S of Reservoir Pond 26x78(93).
Dahurian Larch *L. gmelinii* Rare: collections. Wakehurst Place (Coates Wood) 19x39, 16x40(97); Borde Hill (Stonepit Wood) 19x29(95).
Kurile Larch var. *japonica* Rare: collections. Borde Hill (Stonepit Wood) 16x25(95); Wakehurst Place (Pinetum) 10x39(97).
var. *principis-rupprechtii* At Borde Hill (Stonepit Wood): 19x51(95).
Himalayan Larch *L. griffithii* At Borde Hill (Gores Wood monument): 15x27(96).
Japanese Larch *L. kaempferi* Abundant - mostly plantations. Nymans (Long Woodland Walk) 31x45(98); Normanhurst (estate) 20x74(93); Borde Hill (Warren Wood) 27x64(95); Wakehurst Place (Horsebridge Woods) 27x70(97).
Western Larch *L. occidentalis* Rare: collections. Borde Hill (NE of Tolls) 21x42, 20x52(95).

• *Laurelias look like bay-trees and come from the Andes. Their foliage smells delicious: vanilla, with a hint of orange*

Laurelia sempervirens Rare. Nymans (Top Garden wall; Comber collection 1926) **8x42**(96).

Bay *Laurus nobilis* Abundant. Compton Place 13m(94); The Green, St Leonards (garden, trimmed) 5x45; Bishop's Palace (S edge) 11x31++(97).
'Angustifolia' Rare. Beechwood House (gate) 10x32(97).

Chinese Privet *Ligustrum lucidum* Occasional: larger gardens. Stanmer Park (nursery borders) 10x46@0.3m(94).

Lindera megaphylla Rare: Borde Hill (wall above Pirates Adventure, p1914) **13x52**(95); Wakehurst Place (Westwood Valley, ?) 13x25(97).

SWEET-GUMS

Chinese Sweet-gum *Liquidambar formosana* Rare: large gardens. Borde Hill: Gores Wood (p1941) 15x28, Stephanie's Glade 13x29(95); Alexandra Park (bowling green bank) 14x28+(93).
Sweet-gum *Liquidambar styraciflua* Frequent as a young garden tree. Nymans (House drive) 23x69@0.5m(96); Beechland 21x83(94); Buckham Hill House 17x92@0.3m(94); Horsham Park 17x75(97); Ebernoe House 18x77(97).
'Lane Roberts' In the Memorial Garden, Crawley (two trees): **12x31**(94).
'Worplesdon' At Coates Manor (the original tree): **9x32**(97).

Chinese Tulip Tree *Liriodendron chinense* Occasional. Borde Hill (Garden of Allah, p1913) 19x**87**(95); St Swithuns Close, East Grinstead (turning circle) 17x78(96); Nymans (old tennis lawn) 12x56(96).

Tulip Tree *L. tulipifera* Frequent everywhere. South Hartfield House (splendid bole) 30x157(94); Ely Grange (field) 25x215@1.2m(94); Old Rectory, Newtimber 17x217@0.8m(97); Tilgate Park (Inn) 21x153@1.2m(96); Eridge Park (in line of nine old trees) 23x155@0.9m(94); Danny (cut back; p1760?) 16x153@0.6m(97); Southover Grange 19x121(94).

Chinese Tanbark Oak *Lithocarpus edulis* Rare: collections. Wakehurst Place (Westwood Valley) **14x26**(97).

Maackia amurensis Rare. Borde Hill (drive) 6x25@0.7m(95).

Cucumber Tree *Magnolia acuminata* Occasional: large gardens. Borden Wood 21x43(97); Wakehurst Place (top of Westwood Valley) 19x66(98); Brook House 10x58(93); Little Thakeham 12x46(97); Wildpark, Moulsecoomb (N by Lewes Rd) 12x46(94).

Magnolia 'Anne Rosse' At Nymans (lawn): 6x20@0.4m(96).

Campbell's Magnolia *M. campbellii* Occasional, in big gardens. Leonardslee (Dell) 23x72(96); Wakehurst Place (head of Westwood Valley) 18x91(97); Borde Hill (Azalea Ring) 22x77(95); Nymans (Walled Garden) 18x84@0.3m(96).

var. *alba* Rare: big gardens. Borde Hill (Tolls) **20**x53(95); High Beeches (Queen Mary's Walk) 12x41@0.8m(97); Burnside 14x38(94).

'Charles Raffill' Occasional in big gardens. Nymans (Walled Garden) 13x60(96).

'Wakehurst' At Wakehurst Place (Slips): **11x47**@1.2m(97).

subsp. *mollicomata* Now replacing the type, in big gardens. Borde Hill: Tolls (p1940) 20x39, Garden of Allah 15x43(95).

M. campbellii x subsp. *mollicomata* At Wakehurst Place (Slips): 15x64(97).

M. 'Cecil Nice' At Nymans (Walled Garden): **8x23**@1.2m(96).

M. 'Charles Coates': At Nymans (House drive by nursery) **7x23**(96).

M. dawsoniana Rare: collections. Leonardslee (drive by carpark) 9x26@0.1m(96).

Carnival finery

For a full fifty weeks of the year, no trees appear more staid or solemn than the tree **magnolias**, with their elephant-grey boles and big, clumsy leaves, the fodder of dinosaurs. And yet, for a few days in March, when the famous gardens are seldom visited, carnival time comes round: the trees bedeck themselves in gorgeous, floppy creations of candy-floss pink or satin-white, a thousand Ascot hats on a huge grey hatstand.

It takes thirty years for Campbell's magnolia to flower: planting one in any of today's provisional small gardens would be beside the point, but, for the inheritors of an Edwardian estate, it was a point of duty.

The Sussex High Weald gardens, along with those of Cornwall, now play host to most of the biggest and oldest of these trees. They prefer Cornwall: a late frost, a heat-wave, an easterly wind or lashing rain can - and often do - ruin the fragile display. But, in a good year like 1997, to visit Leonardslee, Borde Hill or, above all, Nymans around Easter is like entering fairyland.

Chinese Evergreen Magnolia *M. delavayi* At Borde Hill (old Kitchen Garden wall, grand old tree, p1911): 10x**57**(95).

Yulan *M. denudata* Rare. Nymans (Walled Garden,var.*purpurascens*) 11x25(96); Beauport Park (opposite 10th tee) 9x**45**(97).

M. fraseri Rare: Leonardslee (head of Dell) 16x41(96); Borde Hill (Garden of Allah) 14x41(95).

Bull Bay *M. grandiflora* Frequent, against old house walls. Brook House 13x46(93); Arundel Castle (by town gate, freestanding) 12x64(97) Goodwood (Hermitage, freestanding) 10x53(97) Southover Grange 11x51(94).

'Exmouth' Occasional. Nymans (house wall) 11x31+19(96); Greyfriars 8x43(94).

'Goliath' Rare. Nymans (house wall) 9x22++(96).

M. hypoleuca Occasional in big gardens. Borde Hill (Garden of Allah) 14x**77**@0.3m(95); Wakehurst Place: S of Slips (cut back) 8x55, Westwood Valley 12x51@1.1m(97).

Northern Japanese Magnolia *M. kobus* Occasional - large and small gardens. Borde Hill (Tolls) 13x38@1.8m(95); Gravetye Manor (East Garden) 9x57@0.5m(97); Victorian Tea Gardens 9x33(95).

M. x loebneri 'Leonard Messel' Occasional in well-planted gardens. Tilgate Park (Peace Garden) 8x24@0.6m(96).

'Merrill' At Wakehurst Place (Pinetum/Slips): 7x32@ground(97).

Big-leaf Magnolia *M. macrophylla* Rare: large gardens. Borden Wood 16x27(97); Leonardslee (top of Mossy Ghyll) 14x27(96).

M. 'Michael Rosse' At Nymans (Top Garden): **12x30**+26(96).

M. officinalis Rare: large gardens. Borde Hill (Tolls) 11x**43**@1m(95).

M. robusta Occasional in large gardens. Borde Hill: Tolls 18x39@0.8m(95), Garden by kiosk (cut back) 8x53++(97); Nymans (old tennis lawn) 12x66@ground(96).

M. rostrata At Borde Hill (garden cottage, p1931): 9x32.

Willow-leaved Magnolia *M. salicifolia* Occasional in large gardens. Wakehurst Place (Westwood Valley) 17x31(97); Tilgate Forest Lodge 13x47(96); Nymans (Wild Garden) 15x34(96).

M. sargentiana Rare; large gardens. Nymans (Walled Garden) 15x**53**(96).

Saucer Magnolia *M. x soulangeana* Abundant in large and small gardens, in mostly shrubby forms. 'Rustica Rubra' (occasional) reaches tree size: Nymans (Walled Garden) 8x24++(96); Tilgate Park (SW) 7x27@1m(97).

'Verbanica' is rare; Borde Hill (behind old Kitchen Garden) **8x36**@0.2m(96).

• *The bigleaf magnolia's oval leaves are gigantic - the size of a broadsheet newspaper*

MAGNOLIAS

M. sprengeri At Wakehurst Place (Horsebridge Woods): 11x36(97).
'Diva' Occasional in well-planted gardens. Borde Hill (Tolls) **22x54**(95).
var. *elongata* At Borde Hill (carpark): 10x21(95).
M. 'Thomas Messel' At Nymans (nursery path): **9x38**@1.2m(96); sister tree by Garden Cottage 13x35(97).
Umbrella Tree *M. tripetala* Occasional in old gardens. Beechland 11x25++(94); Borde Hill (Garden of Allah) 7x28@1m(95).
M. x veitchii Occasional in large gardens. Tilgate Forest Lodge (superb tree) 20x92(96); Nymans (Top Garden) 16x93@0.5m(96).
var. *alba* At Wakehurst Place (Horsebridge Woods): 8x24@0.5m(97).
'Peter Veitch' At High Beeches (below Front Meadow): 13x40@0.3m(97).
Sweet Bay *M. virginiana* Rare. Tilgate Park (mid S) 9x27+26(96).
M. x weiseneri Rare? Nymans (house drive) **8x32**@1.2m +(96).

FLOWERING CRABS

Siberian Crab *Malus baccata* Occasional. Wakehurst Place (house drive) 10x46@1.2m(97).
'Jackii' At Borde Hill (Stephanie's Walk, p1932): **15x65**@0.3m(95).
var. *mandshurica* Quite frequent: gardens and some municipal plantings. Tilgate Park (SW of Inn) 13x79@ground(96); Duckyls Wood 11x48(97).
Garland Crab *M. coronaria* Rare. Lorien 10m(94); Fontridge Manor 7x22(94).
Orchard Apple *M. domestica* Abundant and widely naturalised. 'Reinette Pink Etoilée (with purplish foliage) grows at Stonehurst (Wild Garden) 12x36+36+(97), and Wakehurst Place (depot above Pinetum, original tree) 11x41+36(97).
M. 'Echtermeyer' Rare. Holders 4x20.

Apples sweet and sour

More different kinds of **apple** have been named than there are species of tree in this book. Many are tastier than the apples bought in shops, but unhappily none crop so regularly or store so well.

The modern orchards of the Brede and Rother valleys are as well-drilled as an army on parade; dwarfing rootstocks keep the crowns within reach and close-cropped grey alders or hybrid poplars shelter them. First-year shoots are bedecked with lead weights in winter to promote fruiting, and sometimes bound formatively with multi-coloured tapes, and there is also a touch of flamboyance in the ornamental crabs planted at the end of each row of fruit trees to ensure pollination.

Old orchards, which are scattered around the county, are very different, with sheep grazing the shady collonades of spreading, lichen-clad trees. One at Snailham Hill, now overgrown with brambles, is a home for nightingales, cuckoos, turtle doves and garden warblers.

The truly wild crab is an elusive, thorny inhabitant of ancient woods and medieval hedges. It is often most conspicuous in winter, when the acid-green crabs fall and carpet the ground.

Nothing seems to touch them - which is why the crab is so poor at colonising new sites. Perhaps they naturally appeal to brown bears, or wild boar.

● The Florence crab is very rare in its native Umbria and in cultivation, where the Warnham Court tree is the finest known. Its leaves, unlike other apples, closely resemble those of the wild service

Florence Crab *M. florentina* At Warnham Court (Nursery House paddock, p1956): **10x39**(97).
Japanese Crab *M. floribunda* Abundant: gardens and parks. Pashley Manor (formal garden) 7x27(94); Amberley (garden) 6x40.
M. 'Golden Hornet' Frequent: small gardens and streets. Highdown (Chalk Garden) **9x31**@1m(97).
M. halliana Rare. Cowdray Park (tennis court) 9x30(97).
M. x hartwigii At Wakehurst Place (Westwood Lake): 7x19(97).
Hupeh Crab *M. hupehensis* Occasional: some small gardens and streets. Fontridge Manor (below lake) 11x30(94); Nymans (entrance to Pinetum, Forrest collection) 9x43(96).
M. 'John Downie' Frequent in small gardens. High Beeches 9x42(94); Highdown (carpark, ?) 6x**45**(97).
M. kansuensis At High Beeches (Glade, dying back): 5x16(97).
M. 'Lady Northcliffe' Rare? High Beeches (below Pond) 8x27(97).
M. x micromalus At Borde Hill (Warren Wood): 6x20(95).
M. prattii Rare. Borde Hill (below lake dam, p1926) **10x49**@0.4m(95).
M. prunifolia Probably rare. Stanmer Park (Arboretum, p1964) 5x21(95).
var. *rinki* Rare. Borde Hill (Warren Wood) 6x31@0.1m(96); Stanmer Park (Arboretum, p1964) 6x19(95).
Purple Crab *M. x purpurea* Abundant in streets and gardens in various forms. Fontridge Manor (Arboretum)10x27(94); Winchelsea church 7x39(94). 'Lemoinii' is named at Borde Hill (Warren Wood): 9x25(96).
M. x robusta Abundant in small gardens, in various fruiting forms. Borde Hill (Stephanie's Glade, ?) **15x44**@1.2m(95).
M. x scheideckeri At Tilgate Park (mid S, ?): **9x45**@0.1m(96).
M. sikkimensis At Borde Hill (Warren Wood): 10x23++(96).
Chinese Crab *M. spectabilis.* Occasional? Tilgate Forest Lodge 10x**48**(96).
M. x sublobata At Borde Hill (Gores Wood?): **12x28**(96).
Crab Apple *M. sylvestris* Native; frequent in old woods and hedges. The Mens (The Cut) **17**x29+27(93); Borde Hill (above lake) 16x66(95); Eridge Park (Pinetum) 17x53(94).
M. toringoides Occasional: large and some small gardens. Fontridge Manor (Arboretum)**10**x25(94); Boxgrove Priory 5x30(97); Borde Hill (Pinetum)10x21(95); Sheffield Park (summerhouse) 8x29(94).
M. trilobata Rare: collections. Borde Hill (South Park, Borde Hill Laneside, p1937) 10x37(95); Stanmer Park (Arboretum, p1964) 8x15(94).
Pillar Apple *M. tschonoskii* Frequent municipal tree. Queens Square, Crawley 12x36(97).
M. 'Wintergold' Rare? Wakehurst Place (Westwood Lake) 9x22(97).

Crab apple

M. yunnanensis Occasional: large gardens. Wakehurst Place (Westwood Valley) **10**x41(97); Stanmer Park (nursery borders) 9x26(94); Boxgrove Priory 7x25@0.5m(97).
var. *veitchii* Rare. Borde Hill (Warren Wood) 6x21(95).
M. x zumi Rare. Borde Hill (Warren Wood) 6x21(95).

Mayten *Maytenus boaria* Rare: collections. Nymans (Wild Garden, Comber collection) 11x35(96); Wakehurst Place (depot above Pinetum) 11x31++(97).

Meliosma veitchiorum Rare: collections. Nymans (Top Garden) **14x47**(96).

Medlar *Mespilus germanica* Occasional in old gardens; naturalised in the East. Motcombe Gardens 5x35@1m(94); Linton Crescent, Hastings 5x32@1.2m(93).

Dawn Redwood *Metasequoia glyptostroboides* Becoming abundant. Leonardslee (Dell) **31**x71 and 24x91(96); Sheffield Park (Second/Fourth Lakes) 20x96(94); Cedar Tree Cottage 14x87(97); Stansted Park (Arboretum, mid) 20x84(97); Nymans (top of Pinetum) 20x77(96); Hampden Park 19x66(94).

MULBERRIES

White Mulberry *Morus alba* Rare. Highdown (carpark) 9x22++(97); Bartley Mill 9m(94).
'Pendula' Rare. Wakehurst Place (S of Heath Garden) 4x31@0.6m(97).
Black Mulberry *M. nigra* Frequent in old gardens. West Stoke House 10x62(97); Southover Grange 7x82@1m(94); Old Rectory, Westmeston 8x80(93).

Shakespeare's mulberry

In the garden of East Cliff House in Hastings old town, almost on the beach, is an ancient **mulberry**, practically hidden by the jumbled rooftops.

In the 18th century, the Shakespearean scholar Edward Capel lived here, and the tree is said to be a cutting raised by the actor David Garrick from Shakespeare's own mulberry at Stratford.

Tales abound of the longevity of mulberries but, sad to say, facts are signally lacking: some of the oldest-looking are known to be less than a century old. The biggest in Sussex - the leaning tree in Southover Grange Gardens, Lewes - has added 13% to its girth in as many years.

SOUTHERN BEECHES

Nirre *Nothofagus antartica* Occasional as young tree. Petworth Park (W of carpark) 14x50@0.5m(97).
Coigue *N. dombeyi* Occasional in large gardens. St Roche's Arboretum (bottom entrance) 29x78(97); Petworth Park (W of carpark) 25x92, 24x66(97); South Lodge Hotel (W, top blown out) 13x69(96).
Red Beech *N. fusca* Rare: large gardens. High Beeches (below Pond, p1931) 14x42(97).
N. menziesii Rare: large gardens. Nymans (Top Garden) 14x**78**(96).
var. *microphylla* At Borde Hill (Gores Wood): 14x23(95).
N. menziesii x obliqua At Wakehurst Place (Coates Wood): 11x17(97).
Rauli *N. nervosa* Occasional: large gardens, some belts and plantations. Petworth Park (W of carpark) 24x96@0.4m(97); Chelwood Vachery 21x85(94).
N. nidida At Wakehurst Place (Coates Wood): 10x22(97).
Roblé Beech *N. obliqua* Occasional in gardens, belts etc, mostly as a young tree. South Lodge Hotel (SW) 30x63(96); Tilgate Forest Lodge 22x83(96); Tilgate Park (below walled garden) 25x72, 22x72(96); Coolhurst (roadside, good bole) 25x68(96).
N. pumilio At Wakehurst Place (Coates Wood): 8x18(97).
Black Beech *N. solanderi* Rare. Borde Hill (Gores Wood, p1922) 14x25(95).
var. *cliffortioides* Rare. Wakehurst Place (Heath Garden) 12x59@0.4m(97).

Tupelo *Nyssa sylvatica* Occasional: well-planted gardens. Sheffield Park: East Park 20x48, S of Second Lake 18x**63**(94); High Beeches (below Front Meadow) 11x54@1.8m(97).
'Sheffield Park' At Sheffield Park (original, N of Second Lake): **12x52**(94).

Osmanthus heterophyllus 'Variegatus' Occasional. Buxted Park (garden) 9x22@0.9m+(94).
O. yunnanensis Rare: large gardens. Borde Hill (Long Dell) 11x24(96); Wakehurst Place (above Slips) 8x66@0.1m(97).

Hop Hornbeam *Ostrya carpinifolia* Occasional: large gardens. Petworth Park (House/Pleasure Grounds) 14x81(97); Wakehurst Place (S of Westwood Valley) 14x49(97); Stanmer Park (Arboretum, p1964) 13x37(94); Beauport Park (7th tee) 10x49@1.1m(97).
Japanese Hop Hornbeam *O. japonica* Rare: collections. Borde Hill (S of Little Bentley Wood, p1910) 11x49(95); Wakehurst Place (S of Westwood Valley) 12x59@0.6m(97).
Ironwood *O. virginiana* At Leonardslee (beyond Camellia Walk, ?): 9x15(96).

Sorrel Tree *Oxydendrum arboreum* Occasional - well-planted gardens. Leonardslee (S of Mossy Ghyll) 14x45(96); Newick Park 11x42(94).

Persian Ironwood *Parrotia persica* Quite frequent in gardens. Tilgate Park (mid S) 13x49@1m(96).

Paulownia coreana At Wakehurst Place (above Pinetum): 8x19(97).
P. fortunei At Peasmarsh Place (drive, p1986): 7x15(94).
Empress Tree *P. tomentosa* Occasional. Watergate House 15x66(97); St Johns Road, St Leonards (old nursery; nearly dead) 6x**78**(93); Stansted Park (Arboretum, W side) 14x76(97); Preston Rockery (depot) 11x70(94).

Persea ichangensis At Wakehurst Place (head of Westwood Valley): **12x23**++(97).

CORK TREES

Amur Cork Tree *Phellodendron amurense* Occasional in large gardens. Wakehurst Place (above Pinetum) 16x61(97); Leonardslee (Cross Paths) 14x49(96).
var. *lavallei* Occasional. Borde Hill (Warren Wood) **17**x53(95); Nymans (Garden Cottage) 15x**83**(96); Hollycombe (railway) 17x36+30(97); Stonehurst (Wild Garden) 14x72(97).
Chinese Cork Tree *P. chinense* Rare. Stanmer Park (Arboretum, SE edge, p1964) 9x32(94).
var. *glabriusculum* At Borde Hill (Stephanie's Glade): **14x58**@0.8m(95).
Japanese Cork Tree *P. japonicum* Rare. Wakehurst Place (Westwood Valley) 17x38(97); Tilgate Park (mid S) 10x42@1m(96).

Phillyrea latifolia Infrequent, in old shrubberies, etc; often mistaken for holm oak. St Paul's church, Chichester (in line of 9) **11**x42(97); Stable Cottage 8x51(97); Exceat Visitor Centre (largest of many) 9x46(94).
P.x media At Borde Hill (above Pirates Adventure): **8**x25+23+(95).

Photinia beauverdiana var. *notabilis* Rare. Nymans (beyond pergola) 7x22(96).
P. davidiana Occasional: well-planted gardens. Duckyls Wood 11x16++(97); Leonardslee (below Camellia Walk) 9x39@0.3m(96).
P. serrulata Rare. Knockbridge House 7x15+(94).

SPRUCES

Norway Spruce *Picea abies* Abundant, except on chalk. Nymans (long woodland walk) 38x88(97); St Roche's Arboretum (NW edge) 36x107(97); Hollycombe (estate) 37x81, 31x101(97); Wakehurst Place (Horsebridge Woods) 34x90(97); Leonardslee (above New Pond) 29x99(96).
'Aurea' Rare. Wakehurst Place (Bethlehem Wood) 19x57(98).
'Pendula' A few trees are this form. St Roche's Arboretum (mid/N) 38x98(97).
'Virgata' At Leonardslee (foot of Mossy Ghyll, dying back): **16x46**(96).
Dragon Spruce *P. asperata* Occasional; collections. Borde Hill (Warren Wood) 19x35(95); Wakehurst Place (Pinetum) 17x48(97).
var. *ponderosa* At Borde Hill (Warren Wood): 14x16(95).
Alcock's Spruce *P. bicolor* Occasional; collections. Wakehurst Place (Horsebridge Woods) 24x56(97); Normanhurst (estate road) 18x61(93); Tilgate Park (Peace Garden) 19x56(96); Broadfield Park 13x45(97).
var. *reflexa* At Borde Hill (Gores Wood, ?): **15**x32, 14x37(96).
Sargent's Spruce *P. brachytyla* Occasional; collections. Warnham Court (Pinetum, Wilson collection) 22x49(93); Borde Hill (Gores Wood) 19x56(95); Wakehurst Place (Bethlehem Wood) 18x40(97).
Brewer Spruce *P. breweriana* Occasional in well-planted gardens. Sheffield Park (Conifer Walk, p1910) 18x53(94).
Engelmann Spruce *P. engelmannii* Rare. Wakehurst Place (head of Westwood Valley, 'Fendleri'?) 13x30(97).
f. *glauca* At Gallipot Street (small back garden, vigorous tree): 16x47(97).
White Spruce *P. glauca* Occasional as young tree in the east. Fontridge Manor (gate) 12x27(94).
Sakhalin Spruce *P. glehnii* Rare. Wakehust Place (Bloomer's Valley) 12x31(97); Borde Hill (Gores Wood) 12x30(95).
Hondo Spruce *P. jezoensis* var. *hondoensis* Rare; collections. Borden Wood 26x64(97); Stansted Park (Arboretum, E edge) 13x43(97).
P. koyamae Rare. Borde Hill (Gores Wood) 20x37(95).
Likiang Spruce *P. likiangensis* Occasional; collections. Borde Hill (Warren Wood) 21x45(95); Warnham Court (Pinetum, top lost) 14x73(93); Wakehurst Place (Pinetum) 16x62(97).
Black Spruce *P. mariana* Rare. Stonehurst (valley) 14x29(97) Castle Hill House 10x29(94); High Beeches (Loderi Walk, p1931) 12x25(97).
P. maximowiczii At Borde Hill (Gores Wood): 6x20(96).
Siberian Spruce *P. obovata* At Borde Hill (Gores Wood): 8x16(96).
Serbian Spruce *P. omorika* Occasional in well-planted gardens; a few plantations. Duckyls Wood 24x28(96); Sheffield Park (Conifer Walk) 23x55(94).
Oriental Spruce *P. orientalis* Occasional. Malt House (Pinetum, forks into three at 10m) 30x100(97); Beauport Park: Round Banks 21x106@1.8m(97), Long Shaw 29x95(92); Leonardslee (foot of Mossy Ghyll, fine tree) 28x94(96); Wakehurst Place (Horsebridge Woods) 27x91(97).
'Gracilis' At Dangstein (?): 9x27(97).
Tiger-tail Spruce *P. polita* Occasional; collections. Malt House (Pinetum) 23x70(97).
Colorado Spruce *P. pungens* Rare. Christ's Hospital 14x35(97).
Blue Colorado Spruce var. *glauca* Abundant in small, garden forms. Purple Ridge 20x43(94); Eridge Park (Pinetum, p1880; top lost) 15x55(94); Colemans Hatch church 17x37(94).
'Glauca Pendula' At Lydhurst: 2x27 (80).
P. purpurea Rare; collections. Petworth Park (Pleasure Grounds) 21x52(97); Borde Hill (Pinetum) 20x42(95); Wakehurst Place (Pinetum) 16x47(97).

- *Paulownias are the only tree-sized members of the foxglove family: their coloured towers of blossom betray their ancestry*

- *The Serbian spruce is uniquely tolerant of town air and makes a graceful, narrow pagoda shape*

- *All spruces are scaly, spiny trees, but the tiger-tail is vicious, with needles as sharp as hypodermic syringes*

Red Spruce *P. rubens* Rare. Stonehurst (Wild Garden) 15x36(97).
Schrenk's Spruce *P. shrenkiana* Rare. Borde Hill (North Park cottage garden) **20x45**.
Sitka Spruce *P. sitchensis* Frequent - mostly plantations. Stonehurst (valley) 39x89(97); Claremont School: lake 34x179, cricket field 30x153@1.8m(94); Beauport Park (Babylon Wood, much died back) x159@1m(97); St Roche's Arboretum (S bank) 36x80(97).

A spine-tingler

Some trees demand respect, some provoke affection. The **Sitka spruce** *seems to have a penchant for inspiring sheer, spine-tingling terror. Massed ranks of the tree seem to be too much for all of us.*

Planted in Sussex, like many of the giant conifers which crave clean air and plenty of water, it generally looks thin and sorry for itself, but just occasionally grows into a real, gloomy, brooding presence. One such is probably the largest spruce in eastern England, which is growing in a particularly moist and sheltered valley by the lake dam at Claremont School, outside Hastings (p.12).

Morinda Spruce *P. smithiana* Occasional. Malt House (Pinetum) 27x78(97); Stansted Park (Arboretum, moribund) 23x116(97).
Sikkim Spruce *P. spinulosa* Rare. Borde Hill (Gores Wood) 23x45(95).
P. wilsonii Rare. Wakehurst Place (Pinetum) 17x40(97).

Pieris formosa var. *forrestii* In well-planted gardens. Borde Hill (Gores Wood) 8x23+23++(96).

PINES

Chinese White Pine *Pinus armandii* Rare. The Hyde (Pinetum) 26x59, 25x79(96); Leonardslee (Mossy Ghyll) 23x66(97).
Knobcone Pine *P. attenuata* Rare: collections. Wakehurst Place (Horsebridge Woods) 18x43(97); Leonardslee (Coronation Garden) 16x31(96).
Mexican White Pine *P. ayacahuite* Rare? Alexandra Park (model railway/lawn) 14x48(93).
Jack Pine *P. banksiana* Rare. Stansted Park (Arboretum, SE fence) 11x32(97).
Arolla Pine *P. cembra* Rare. Warnham Court (Wild Garden by road) 18x34(97); Birch Farm Nursery 12x39@0.5m(95).
Shore Pine *P. contorta* Frequent: belts and plantations (mostly var. *latifolia*). Warnham Court (Pinetum) 21x96(93).
Big-cone Pine *P. coulteri* Occasional in big gardens. Wakehurst Place (Sands study centre) 23x88(97); Fontridge Manor (entrance lawn) 15x71(94).
Japanese Red Pine *P. densiflora* Rare. Little Fontridge 10x34(94).
Short-leaf Pine *P. echinata* At Wakehurst Place (above Westwood Lake): 6x16(97).
Limber Pine *P. flexilis* At Lorien: 8x20(94).
P. greggii At Goodwood (High Wood): **18x82**(97).
Holford Pine *P. x holfordiana* Occasional. Worth Lodge Forest (plantation) 26x43(96); Borde Hill (Gores Wood, branchy) 23x105(95).
Jeffrey Pine *P. jeffreyi* Occasional in large gardens. Warnham Court (Pinetum) 33x91(93); Malt House (Pinetum) 32x94(97); Ashdown House School 27x71(94).
Bosnian Pine *P. leucodermis* Occasional in big gardens. Wakehurst Place: Pinetum 23x79, Sands study centre (forks) 18x89(97).
Masson Pine *P. massoniana* At Wakehurst Place (Pinetum): 8x23(97).
Montezuma Pine *P. montezumae* Occasional; collections. Sheffield Park (N of First Lake, lovely tree, p1910) 16x86(94).
var. *hartwegii* At Wakehurst Place: Pinetum **20x60**, below Pinetum 20x58(97).
Western White Pine *P. monticola* At Wakehurst Place (Pinetum): 14x42(97).
Bishop Pine *P. muricata* Occasional. Borde Hill (Warren Wood, long bole) **31**x97(95); Ewhurst church (branchy) 11x75(94); Flatropers Wood (N path) 12x65(94).
Austrian Pine *P. nigra* subsp. *nigra* Frequent; shelterbelts near coast etc. Worth Abbey 33x113(96); Normanhurst (estate) 25x131(93);Handcross Park (lawn) 23x167@0.4m(98).
Corsican Pine var. *maritima* Abundant; plantations and belts. Eridge Park (Pinetum) 34x108(94); Normanhurst (lake dam) 24x126(93); Buchan Country Park (Douster Pond dam) 33x105(97).
Crimean Pine var. *pallasiana* Occasional. St Roche's Arboretum (bottom glade) 39x111(97); Hollycombe (estate) 26x129(97).
Pyranean Pine var. *salzmannii* Rare: collections. Borde Hill (S of Tolls, ?) 19x73(96).
Japanese White Pine *P. parviflora* Occasional. Leonardslee (Top Garden) 19x54(96); Tilgate Park (Peace Garden) 11x42(96).
Mexican Pine *P. patula* Occasional as a beautiful young tree in well-planted gardens. Watermill House (dying back) 8x30(95).
Macedonian Pine *P. peuce* Occasional. Leonardslee (Mossy Ghyll) 20x61(96); Stansted Park (Arboretum, E fence) 14x55; Wakehurst Place (Pinetum) 17x61+52(97).
Maritime Pine *P. pinaster* Occasional; in several small gardens. Ashburnham (S of Broad Water) 31x107(93); Sheffield Park (N of Second Lake, p1797?) 27x110(94); South Wood, Catsfield 19x110(93); Mountfield church (laneside) 23x84(94).
Stone Pine *P. pinea* Quite frequent; many small gardens. Ashburnham (the Grove) 17x81(93).
Western Yellow Pine *P. ponderosa* Occasional in bigger gardens. Leonardslee (Hill Garden) 31x87(96); Borde Hill (Warren Wood, British Columbian seed 1917) 30x66(95).
var. *scopulorum* At Wakehurst Place (Pinetum): 10x30(97).
Monterey Pine *P. radiata* Frequent, especially near coasts. Ashburnham (S of Front Water) 37x129(93); Normanhurst (estate; long buttressed bole) 23x200(93); Borden Wood 29x191@0.5m(97); Brambletye School 26x189@0.3m(94); Selham House 34x150.

• *Along with its look-alike, the Monterey pine, the Bishop grows much faster in Sussex than on the few Californian cliffs where it is native*

• *The Mexican pine's grass-green silky hanging needles make it the most beautiful of pines, but it is not reliably hardy in Sussex*

PINES

Scots pine

Red Pine *P. resinosa* Rare. Lorien (?) 14x39(94).
Northern Pitch Pine *P. rigida* Rare; collections. Wakehurst Place: Pinetum 14x45, Sands study centre 13x71(97); Leonardslee (Coronation Garden) 14x26(96).
P. sibirica At Borde Hill: 11x20(95).
Weymouth Pine *P. strobus* Occasional as young tree. Hollycombe (estate, much broken) 23x78, 15x97(97).
'Pendula' At Leonardslee (below Restaurant): 8x22(96).
Scots Pine *P. sylvestris* Abundant and naturalised on light soils. Ashburnham (Walk Wood) 31x71(93); Bartley Mill Wood (just below road) 26x135(94); Pashley Manor (lawn) 20x120(94).
'Aurea' Rare. Stonehurst (below rockery - awarded AGM in 1964) 12x40(97); Heaselands 12x33(96).
'Pendula' At Warnham Court (Wild Garden): 6x15(97).
'Watereri' Rare. Birch Farm Nursery 9x27@0.5m(95).
Chinese Pine *P. tabuliformis* Rare. Lorien 12x22(94).
Loblolly Pine *P. taeda* Rare. Wakehurst Place (Pinetum) 15x55(97).
P. taiwanensis At Borde Hill (Gores Wood): 8x16(95).
Kuro-matsu *P. thunbergii* Rare: collections. Borde Hill (Azalea Ring, Japanese seed 1890) **27**x75(95).
Bhutan Pine *P. wallichiana* Quite frequent as young tree, in many small gardens. St Roche's Arboretum (centre, N side) 31x91(97).

Pittosporum dallii At Wakehurst Place (Specimen Beds): 6x27++(97).
Kohuhu *P. tenuifolium* Occasional in gardens near coasts. Church Lane, Funtington (line of trees) 9x30++; Sunte Avenue, Lindfield 6x32@0.5m.
'Silver Queen' Occasional near coasts. Bishop's Palace 7x41@0.1m, 6x21+(97).

PLANES

Platanus 'Augustine Henry' At Warnham Court (Nursery House paddock): 21x46(97).
London Plane *P.* x *hispanica* Frequent; the biggest are all by the Western Rother. Woolbeding House (long straight bole; 30x100 in 1903) 37x173(97); Stopham House (burry) 28x240(97); Stedham Mill (forks) 33x232@1.2m(97); Casters Brook 29x217(97); Trotton (N tree by Bridge) 28x195(97); Cowdray Park (Lime Bottom) 29x199(97); Horsham Park (dying back) 30x179(96).
Oriental Plane *P. orientalis* Less frequent than London Plane. Borde Hill (Lullings Ghyll) 28x110(95); Petworth Park (Upper Pond) 18x152@0.5m(97); Woolbeding House (two ancient trees with layered branches, the second spreading over 58m) 20x137, 17x127@1m (97); Wiston Post Office 21x125(97).
P. 'Pyramidalis' Occasional; most planes in Hastings are this form. Hove Park **24x126**(93); Alexandra Park (filter beds) 24x116(93).

● *The podocarps are a large group of tropical conifers. The willow podocarp's broad, glossy leaves are a bizarre spectacle in Sussex*

Plum-Yew *Podocarpus andinus* Occasional. Park Way, Easebourne (cottage verge) 12x**66**@0.9m, 12x64@0.3m(97); Midhurst Methodist church carpark (cut back) 8x37++(97).
Manio *P. nubigenus* At Borde Hill (Warren Wood): 6x20(95).
Willow Podocarp *P. salignus* Occasional, in a few small and many big gardens. Hollycombe (estate) 14x37+36+32(97); Brightling Hall 9x51@1.1m(94); South Lodge Hotel (rockery) 11x56@0.3m(96); Beauport Park (caravan park) 12x34+27(96).
Totara *P. totara* Rare; collections. Lydhurst 10x15+14 (80); Leonardslee (Top Garden) 5x18(96).

POPLARS

● *Balsam poplars like the tacamahac are often grown for the scent of their expanding buds, but can reach a hundred feet in 20 years*

Populus x *acuminata* At Stanmer Park (Arboretum, p1964): 16x31(94).
White Poplar *P. alba* Abundant, especially on the coast. Borde Hill (behind Naldred Farmhouse) 25x81, 19x93(95).
Bolle's Poplar 'Pyramidalis' Occasional municipal tree. Penns-in-the-Rocks (very slender; 11m in 1984) 22x26(94); Ewhurst church 10x28(94); East Court (Meridian Hall terrace) 14x23(96).
'Richardii' Occasional. Old Malling Deanery 6x23(94).
P. 'Balsam Spire' Abundant: belts and plantations. Tentworth Woods (plantation) 31x59(97).
Tacamahac *P. balsamifera* Occasional. Stanmer Park (Arboretum, p1964) 21x40(94).
Berlin Poplar *P.* x *berolinensis* Rare. Wakehurst Place (below Pergola) 30x86(97); Hollycombe (estate) 25x55(97).
Balm of Gilead *P.* x *candicans* Rare. Ashburnham (Winter Garden) 18x45(93).
'Aurora' Frequent in small gardens. Stanmer Park (Arboretum, grove) 16x34(94); Memorial Gardens, Crawley 14x39(97); St Leonards Gardens 15x34(93).
Grey Poplar *P. canescens* Frequent in the countryside. Borde Hill (lake dam, p1958) 30x86(95); Plashett Park 26x150@1m(94); Groombridge Place (Sussex bank of Grom) 29x97, 22x123(94).
P. x 'Eugenei' Occasional? in belts and plantations. Great Wood, Battle (lower Marley Lane gate) 27x80(94).
P. x 'Gelrica' At Stanmer Park (Arboretum, p1964): 21x40(95).
P. x *generosa* Rare. Borde Hill (outside Peartree Wood) 29x93, 27x96(95).
Chinese Necklace Poplar *P. lasiocarpa* Occasional - large gardens. Warnham Court (Nursery House paddock) 19x53(97).
P. x 'Marilandica' Rare? Stanmer Park (Arboretum, p1964) 24x43(95).
Black Poplar *P. nigra* subsp. *betulifolia* Occasional: mostly as young tree in belts. Single large trees include: Manor Cottage, Bury 27x115; Old Malling Deanery (river bank, cut back after 1987) 10x201, 19x195(94); Isfield Church 25x135(94) (two more old trees just up-river); Sheffield Bridge 18x115 (W side of bridge; young tree opposite); William Parker School (above running track) 23x119(93); Cowdray Park: back of Benbow Pond layby, 15x108@1m, A272 nearly into Midhurst 23x102(97); Bell Lane Recreation Ground (vigorous young tree) 25x98(94); Hotham Park (SW side, pair) 21x87(97); Forest Row (Medway above village, one of five trees) 19x112(95).
Female Lombardy Poplar *P. nigra* 'Gigantea' Frequent. Stedham (fishermen's carpark) 31x78(97); Barcombe (TQ413141) 25x111@1.2m(94).

Lombardy Poplar 'Italica' Abundant. Stedham (river bank towards Iping) 32x76(97); Sheffield Park Farm 31x109(94); Crooked Lane, Birdham 23x102(97).

Railway Poplar *P*. x 'Regenerata' Abundant everywhere as mature tree. Wakehurst Place (Pinetum) 36x120(97); Railwayland, Lewes 15x**191**(93); Alexandra Park (upper Shornden Reservoir, broken 1997) x184@1.8m(93); Old Roar Ghyll (Coronation Wood side) 36x101(93); Homefield Park 25x139(96).

P. x 'Robusta' Abundant in belts and plantations. Borde Hill (North Park pond) 34x109(95); Wakehurst Place (path to Sands) 30x116(98).

Cottonwool snowstorms

Remember the **railway poplar**. One of several hybrids between the European black poplar and American cottonwoods, this tree was first noted in France in 1814, and has for many years been one of the most abundantly grown and conspicuous trees in Sussex. Few floras mention it; the common name was only coined by Alan Mitchell in 1974. But it is completely distinct - with its cottonwool snowstorm of seeds in July; its curiously metallic sea-green foliage, blending with nothing; its fragile, spidersweb tracery of blonde shoots in winter; and, above all, in October, when the inner leaves fall and a fringe of big leaves hangs on to silhouette it, just as if a flock of starlings had alighted.

The biggest known railway poplar, appropriately, is one of several old pollards in the Railwayland Local Nature Reserve at Lewes, in the wooded corner nearest the station; its bole forks into three at head-height. Another, by the upper Shornden reservoir in Alexandra Park, is almost as large, and was pollarded 8m up. In a storm in January 1997, the very hollow bole was shattered just below this point, but, as it was not threatening anyone, the very dead-looking, jagged snag was left alone. That spring, the old tree burst into new life, growing great bunches of two-metre shoots all over itself.

Another railway poplar of the same planting, by the upper duckpond in the park, was for many years the only known host in East Sussex for toothwort, a leafless plant which parasitises tree roots and is visible only in April when its eerie, flesh-pink flower-spikes appear. Four more very tall railway poplars at the bottom of Old Roar

Ghyll, adjoining the park, have also proved to support toothwort, which was presumably first carried into the vice-county with this batch of trees. It has now spread to a number of other trees in the ghyll.

The railway poplar's place has, alas, been usurped by faster and straighter hybrids, and no nurseries now stock it; it is not long-lived, and, in a hundred years, the Sussex landscape will be empty of it.

The tree with which the railway poplar has generally been confused, the black Italian poplar, always seems to have been rare in Sussex - it is far less tolerant of maritime exposure. Trees in sheltered spots, however, are singularly magnificent, with towering grey boles and vast, dark heads of foliage. The young one at Arundel, on the river plain in the lea of the castle, is typical of the best. It is probably the tallest broadleaved tree in Sussex (an accolade the black Italian poplar can claim in many counties) but is still growing. It is best viewed from Mill Lane, and stands behind the avenue of limes.

The American parent of these poplars (P. deltoides) no longer appears to be in cultivation in Sussex. A tree of the cultivar 'Carolin', planted at Danny around 1760, was 34m tall in 1909 and had over 50 trunks, rooting and arising again at distances of up to 34m from the original stem. Bits of it were still alive in the 1980s, but in 1997 only one rotting fragment was preserved.

The British parent, P. nigra subsp. betulifolia, (p. 39), is a scarce tree which deserves to be common. It germinates naturally only in the wet mud of river-valleys, so it is hard to tell whether it is truly a native. A handful of trees in Sussex, typically rugged and characterful, grow on the banks of the Ouse and the Medway, but are more likely to represent old plantings. The biggest and oldest, both trimmed back, grow by the Ouse at Old Malling Deanery, and can best be seen from the footpath on the opposite embankment. A third is now a stump, and the equal distances between the three strongly suggest that they were placed here.

More recently, the black poplar's fortunes have enjoyed an upturn, and there are some 400 trees between 10 and 40 years old around the county. The tree grows furiously and has a dense, broad, leafy crown, even in exposure and on poor dry soil - there are two by Pagham Harbour at Church Norton and one in a front garden at Peacehaven. Most of the younger trees are growing in shelterbelts (most notably around Snaylham Farm near Icklesham). Such a spreading giant is the least suitable of trees for this purpose and it is likely that most were supplied in error for Lombardy poplars, which are fastigiate forms of the same species.

Black Italian Poplar *P*. x 'Serotina' Occasional. Arundel Castle 39x142(97); Eridge Park (Pinetum) 33x150(94).

P. x 'Serotina Aurea' Occasional as younger tree. Warnham Court (Nursery House) 22x76(97).

Aspen *P. tremula* Native; frequent. Gravetye Forest (TQ366346) 24x53(97); Stumbletts Wood, Catsfield (in grove) 24x41, 23x48(94).

'Erecta' Rare. Newton Road, Lindfield 12x15(97).

'Pendula' Rare. Hickmans Lane, Lindfield 4x22(97).

Western Balsam Poplar *P. trichocarpa* Occasional as old tree, in belts etc. Dolphins Leisure Centre (end of line) 27x96(96); Station Approach, Horsted Keynes 27x82(98).

'Fritzi Pauley' At Wakehurst Place (Horsebridge Woods): 18x24(97).

'Scott Pauley' At Wakehurst Place (Horsebridge Woods): 16x21(97).

P. yunnanensis At Wakehurst Place (bog garden, K Rushforth collection): 10x25(97).

• **Aspen leaves flutter in the slightest breeze to increase photosynthesis. Trees of ill repute, they are said to have provided the timber of the Cross**

Prunus 'Accolade' Frequent municipal tree. Heaselands 9x38(96); Orchard Road, Burgess Hill (moribund) 7x**53**(97); York Road, Tilgate 8x47(96).

P. 'Amanogawa' Abundant street and garden tree. Snell Hatch Cemetery 10x22+(97); Firle Rd, Bexhill 7x35@1m; Wykeham Road, Hastings (street tree) 7x30(94).

P. 'Asano' Rare. Whyte Cottage 5x18@1m.

Wild Cherry *P. avium* Native; also planted abundantly. Stumblewood Common (TQ408307) 24x50(94); Barnes Wood, Whatlington (decayed tree in Corsican pine plantation) 18x101(95); Park Wood, Hellingly (spreading tree, TQ603123) 15x101(93); Beauport Park (15th fairway, now recumbent) x116 (81).

'Pendula' At Sedgewick Park: **11x33**(97).

FLOWERING CHERRIES

• **There are many kinds of fruiting cherry in cottage gardens, bred from the wild and sour cherries**

FLOWERING CHERRIES

'Plena' Frequent amenity tree. Alexandra Park (above upper Shornden Reservoir) 18x40+34(97); Northgate Middle School 15x74@1.2m(97); Withdean Park 10x60(94).

P. x blireana Frequent in suburban gardens. Linton Road, Hastings 6x35.

Grey Cherry *P. canescens* Rare. Mill Brook Farm 7x18(94).

Myrobalan Plum *P. cerasifera* Abundant and naturalised. Laughton church 12x27(94); Hurst Mill (below tennis court) 5x54@0.9m(97).

'Hessei' Rare. Banks Farm 6x18@1.1m(94).

'Lindsayi' At Stanmer Park (Arboretum, p1964): 9x27(95).

Pissard Plum 'Pissardii' Abundant in suburbia, along with 'Nigra'. Alexandra Park (Bohemia gates) 11x23(94); St Pauls church, Chichester 8x63@0.4m(97).

Rhex's Cherry *P. cerasus* 'Rhexii' Rare. Nymans (Wild Garden) 7x20(96); Cuckfield church 5x51(96).

P. conradinae Rare. Alexandra Park (upper duckpond) **8x24**(93).

Himalayan Bird Cherry *P. cornuta* Rare. Warnham Court (Wild Garden, ?) 12x46(97).

Plum

Plum *P. domestica.* Abundant and naturalised. The commonest form in the wild is the bullace, subsp. *insititia*: Caneheath (roadside) 10x37(94); Sedgewick Park 9x43@1.2m(97).

Almond *P. dulcis* Frequent in small gardens. Rosebery Avenue, Eastbourne 8x35@0.8m.

'Praecox' At Stanmer Park (Arboretum, p1964): 5x16@1.2m(95).

P. 'Fugenzo' Occasional. Alexandra Park (Thorpe's Wood, p1935) **8x62**(93).

Flag Cherry P. 'Hatazakura' Rare. Alexandra Park (bandstand?) **7x33**(94).

P. x hillieri Rare. Borde Hill (carpark, p1942?) 9x46(95); Warnham Court (Wild Garden, bole torn across) 7x43(97).

P. 'Hilling's Weeping' Rare. Hurst Mill (track) 2x21(97).

P. 'Hokusai' Occasional in small gardens. Ashdown Drive, Tilgate 8x45(97).

P. 'Horinji' Rare. Frant church 5x22(96).

P. 'Ichiyo' Occasional; street plantings in Hastings and Bexhill. Elphinstone Junior School 8x40(94); Birk Dale, Bexhill 6x52(97).

Fuji Cherry *P. incisa* Occasional in large gardens. Wakehurst Place (Specimen Beds) **9x66**@0.1m(97); Stanmer Park (nurseries) 8x37@1m(95).

'February Pink' Rare. Stanmer Park (Arboretum, p1964) 6x18(95).

'Praecox' At Stanmer Park (Arboretum, p1964): 5x15(95).

Hill Cherry *P. jamasakura* Occasional - large gardens. Duckyls Wood 19x28+(96); Worthing Crematorium (drive to old house, very spreading) 8x59(96); Borde Hill (Gores Wood monument, p1937) 17x43@0.1m(95).

P. 'Jo Nioi' Occasional. Castle Hill House 7m(94).

P. 'Kanzan' Abundant. Pashley Manor (western lawns) **14**x56@0.9m(94); Alexandra Park (war memorial) 10x70(93); Winchelsea church 7x73@0.5m(94).

P. 'Kiku Shidare Zakura' Abundant in small gardens. Alley Cottage 3x25.

Cherry Laurel *P. laurocerasus* Abundant and widely naturalised. Borden Wood 18x40@1m++(97).

'Magnoliifolia' Rare? Hollycombe (railway, spreading across 30m) 8x**50**@1m(97).

Portugal Laurel *P. lusitanica* Abundant and naturalised. Beauport Park (behind Hotel) 13x38(92); Ashburnham (above Ironspring) 10x47, 12x62@0.5m(97).

Manchurian Cherry *P. maackii* Occasional. Nymans (North Park) 9x34(96); Stanmer Park (Arboretum, p1964) 8x23(94); Woodvale Crematorium (N side) 7x19(95).

St Lucie Cherry *P. mahaleb* Rare. Stanmer Park (Arboretum, p1964) 6x15(95).

P. 'Mikuruma-gaeshi' Rare. Malt House (drive) 6x**35**(97).

P. 'Ojochin' Occasional - several in Brighton. Morley Lodge 8x42(94); Woodvale Crematorium (N bank) 7x29(95); Wildpark, Moulsecoomb (Lewes Rd side) 6x32(95).

Bird cherry

Bird Cherry *P. padus* Occasional. 'Watereri' is much planted in streets and parks: Duckyls Wood 18x48(96); Borde Hill (below lake) 12x65(95).

P. 'Pandora' A few old street trees; now in commerce again. Fairlawne Crescent, East Grinstead **8x66**(96); Heathcote Drive, East Grinstead 8x55(96); Ashdown Drive, Tilgate 8x56(96).

P. 'Pink Perfection' Frequent. Southover Grange 9x39(94); Chiddinglye 7x**43**(96).

P. pleiocerasus At Borde Hill (South Park, Borde Hill Laneside) 6x46@0.1m(95).

P. rufa Rare: collections. Highdown 6x16(93).

Sargent Cherry *P. sargentii* Frequent everywhere. Leonardslee (below restaurant) 13x**90**(96); The Hyde 10x85@1m(96).

'Rancho' Occasional municipal tree. Brunswick Court **12**x26(97).

P. x schmittii Occasional as a street tree. Borde Hill (Pinetum, grown as *P. canescens*) **20**x56@0.8m(95); Birk Dale, Bexhill 9x31(94); St Helens Rd, Hastings 10x31(93).

Black Cherry *P. serotina* Occasional. Newick Park **19**x**104**@0.1m(94).

'Pendula' In Hurst Green (opposite Delmas Antiques): 10x48.

Tibetan Cherry *P. serrula* In many well-planted gardens; street trees in Bexhill. Duckyls Wood 9x36@0.9m(96); Firle Rd, Bexhill (street planting) 5x34@1.1m(97).

P. serrulata Occasional. Leonardslee: south drive **8**x35, below new house 5x71@0.6m(96); Funtington church 5x**77**@0.2m(97).

P. 'Shirofugen' Frequent. The Hyde 8x56(96); High Beeches (below pond) 8x56@1.2m(94); Chiddinglye 6x56(96).

P. 'Shirotae' Frequent. Heaselands 7x51@0.1m(96); Milton Mount Gardens (SW) 5x39(97).

P. 'Shogetsu' Frequent. Pashley Manor (east lawn) 5x32(94); Highdown (Lower Garden) 4x36(98).

P. 'Shujaku' At Stonehurst (below rockery, ?) 8x28(97).

Naden *P. x sieboldii* At Beech Hurst Gardens (far NW corner, fine tree) **7x45**@1.2m(96).

Oshima Cherry *P. speciosa* Rare. Borde Hill (Warren Wood) 8x24@0.9m(96).

Blackthorn

Blackthorn *P. spinosa* Native; abundant. Dumpford Park Farm (in spinney, SU823213) **12**x17(97).

P. 'Spire' Occasional street tree. Cedar Tree Cottage 10x39@0.4m(97) Wren Court, Tilgate 8x22(97).

P. subhirtella var. *ascendens* At Standen (Quarry Garden): 8x25(97).

Winter Cherry 'Autumnalis' Abundant in small gardens, along with 'Autumnalis Rosea'. Alexandra Park (St Helens Rd by bowling green) 10x38(93); Combermere Road, St Leonards 7x69@0.9m(94).

'Pendula Rosea' Occasional. Nymans (Walled Garden) 5x**59**(96).

'Pendula Rubra' Occasional. Battle Abbey (behind Dormitory) 2x33(98).
P. 'Sumizome' Rare. Hurst Mill (millrace,?) 11x36(97).
Great White Cherry *P.* 'Tai Haku' Frequent. Moor House 5x53(97); Ifield Avenue, Crawley 5x51(97); Hurst Mill (drive by house) 5x43(97).

Back from the dead

'Tai Haku', the **great white cherry** of old Japan, has flowers almost as big as roses, set off by ruby young leaves.

In Japan itself, the tree had become a legend, known only from 18th century portraits. Then, in 1923, Collingwood Ingram, the century's great cherry-connoisseur, happened in a French hotel to bump into an Englishwoman who had in her garden a cherry, just clinging on to life, which had been brought from Japan in 1900. The tree,

Captain Ingram soon came to realise, was the long-lost 'Tai Haku'.

The garden is generally claimed to have been in Sussex, but according to a surviving acquaintance it was actually just over the Kent border in Appledore, and close to Ingram's home at Benenden.

Wherever the exact location may have been, all the 'Tai Hakus' in the world have been propagated from this one mysterious survivor.

There is a whole avenue of street trees along Ifield Avenue in Crawley.

P. 'Ukon' Frequent. Shackleton Rd, Crawley (on green) 8x48(96); Leonardslee (Wallaby pen, cut back) 5x**55**(96); Rye Salts (A259 side) 8x40(96); Malt House (drive) 6x45(97).
P. 'Umineko' Becoming frequent as a street tree. Stanmer Park (Arboretum, p1964) 7x22(95).
P. 'Yedo Zakura' At The Hyde: 6x**37**(96).
Yoshino Cherry *P. x yedoensis* Frequent in small gardens. Horsham Nursery School 8x60.
P. 'Yokihi' Behind Five Acres, Northgate (?) 5x31, 4x33 etc.(97).

Golden Larch *Pseudolarix amabilis* Occasional: collections. Wakehurst Place: Bloomer's Valley 14x56(98), Slips 12x59(97); Leonardslee (Daffodil Lawn) 10x66(96).

Japanese Douglas Fir *Pseudotsuga japonica* Rare, collections. Borde Hill (Tolls) **12**x16(95).
Big-cone Douglas Fir *P. macrocarpa* Rare. Borde Hill (Gores Wood) 19x38(95).
Douglas Fir *P. menziesii* Abundant in the High Weald, in gardens and forestry. St Roche's Arboretum (N side of valley, mid) 44x124(97); Normanhurst (four in park the same size, with dead tops) 29x153(93); Beauport Park (below Hotel, died back from 40m) 34x155@0.8m(97); Eridge Park (Pinetum) 36x140; Wakehurst Place (Westwood Valley) 39x93(97); Chelwood Beacon (plantation below Vachery) 39x71(94); and see 'Tall Trees'. 'Stairii' At Beechland: 13x42(94).
Blue Douglas Fir var. *glauca* Occasional. Borde Hill (South Park, Borde Hill Laneside) 26x43(96); Tilgate Park (Pinetum) 22x46(96); Alexandra Park (below Buckshole, very blue) 15x41@1.2m(93).

Caucasian Wingnut *Pterocarya fraxinifolia* Occasional in parks and big gardens. Highfields Park (forest of stems) 21x244@0.5m(94); Borde Hill (top of Lullings Ghyll) 19x109@1.7m(95); Gravetye Forest (head of lake, suckering widely) 18x92@1.8m(97).
P. *paliurus* At Borde Hill (Gores Wood, ?, p1932): **13**x16(96).
Hybrid Wingnut *P. x rehderana* Occasional. Borde Hill (South Park) 21x108, 19x123(95); Wakehurst Place (Park beyond Specimen Beds) 16x123@1m(98).
P. *rhoifolia* At Borde Hill (Lullings Ghyll): 19x47(95).
Chinese Wingnut *Pterocarya stenoptera* Rare. Hollycombe (gardens, sparse) 18x88(97).

Pterostyrax hispida Rare: large gardens. Hollycombe (railway) **12**x46+(97); Wakehurst Place (head of Westwood Valley, lovely tree) 11x34(97).

Callery Pear *Pyrus calleryana* Rare: collections ('Chanticleer' now popular as municipal tree). Borde Hill (top of Warren Wood) 14x45(95).
'Bradford' At West Dean Gardens (West Lawn): **9**x25(97).
P. 'Chojira' At Borde Hill (Warren Wood): **15**x**47**@0.5m(95).
Wild Pear *P. communis/P. pyraster* Occasional - merges into cultivated pears. Alexandra Park (bank W of tea-rooms) 17x83(93); Denne Park (footpath from Horsham, TQ168294) 11x95(96); Wartling (field, TQ657093) 12x69(94).
P. *cossonii* At Borde Hill (Warren Wood): **17**x51(95).
P. *glabra* At Nymans (Wild Garden, ?, died back): 8x**41**(96).
Snow Pear *P. nivalis* Occasional as a young tree. Alexandra Park (over stream from hard tennis) 8x18(93); Gensing Gardens 7x20(93).
P. *pashia* Rare: large gardens. Nymans (Wild Garden) 12x32(96); Borde Hill (Warren Wood, Forrest collection) 11x42@0.8m(95).
var. *kumaoni* At Wakehurst Place (above Pinetum): 11x27+(97).
Sand Pear *P. pyrifolia* At Wakehurst Place (behind Restaurant): **12**x42@0.5m(91).
Silver-leaved Pear *P. salicifolia* Frequent (always 'Pendula'). Sheffield Park (S of First Lake, p1924) 8x35(94); Wildpark, Moulsecoomb (Lewes Rd) 7x25(94); Buckingham Park 8x27(94).
Ussurian Pear *P. ussuriensis* Rare. Borde Hill (below Lake, var. *hondoensis*, Wilson collection) **10**x58@0.5m, 9x**75**@1.1m(95).

PEARS

• The truly wild pear is a big tree with fruit as hard as marbles. Most roadside and hedgerow pears have crossed with orchard trees

OAKS

- *The Beechwood Turkey oak is one of the biggest oak trees in Britain*

- *The kermes oak is the food of the kermes insect, the source of scarlet grain dye: the Dyers' Company has three sprigs for its crest*

- *The original Lucombe oak was felled by its discoverer, William Lucombe, to make his coffin, but Lucombe lived to 102 and the boards rotted. Fortunately others were propagated so that he could be buried in timber from a second tree*

Sessile Oak

Japanese Evergreen Oak *Quercus acuta* Rare. Borde Hill (Gores Wood, p1942) 11m(95).

Japanese Sawtooth Oak *Q. acutissima* Rare. Borde Hill (Stonepit Wood) 16x46(95); Petworth Park (Park W of Lower Pond) 13x50(97).

Californian Live Oak *Q. agrifolia* Rare. Borde Hill (Stonepit Wood, p1936) 13x23+16+(95); Peasmarsh Place (p1976) 7x22@1.2m(94).

White Oak *Q. alba* (x *robur*?) Rare. West Dean Gardens (Wild Garden) 11x46(97).

Golden Oak *Q. alnifolia* Rare. Leonardslee (Mossy Ghyll): 5x16(96).

Swamp White Oak *Q. bicolor* Rare. Warnham Court (Nursery House paddock) 13x32(97).

Mirbeck's Oak *Q. canariensis* Occasional: large gardens. Leonardslee (path below Cox's Walk) 27x70(96); Alexandra Park (oak bank) 26x109(93); Sheffield Park (East Park) 24x90(94).

Q. canariensis x robur Occasional. Knockbridge House 16x30(94).

Chestnut-leaved Oak *Q. castaneifolia* Occasional: large gardens. Beauport Park (Hollow Wood) 25x155(97); Borde Hill (Stonepit Wood/lake) 23x80(95).

Turkey Oak *Q. cerris* Abundant; naturalised on light soils. Beechwood House (magnificent tree) 38x214(97); Hamsey Manor 26x197(94); Framfield (field W of church) 28x198(94); St Roches Arboretum (bottom entrance, slender and straight) 36x129(97).

'Laciniata' Rare? Sedgewick Park (park) 24x122(97); Borde Hill (by Great Bentley Wood) 24x100@1.2m(95).

Kermes Oak *Q. coccifera* Rare. Borde Hill: Stonepit Wood **12x27**, outside The Explorer 8x**51**@0.5m(95); Highdown (Chalk Garden) 6x26@0.3m(97).

Scarlet Oak *Q. coccinea* Frequent: parks and larger gardens. Borden Wood **28x89**(97); Blackwell Recreation Ground 23x85(96); Alexandra Park (model railway) 25x68(93); Hammerwood Park (estate) 21x85(94); Ebernoe House 23x87(97); Hollycombe (garden) 24x83(97); Borde Hill (south of Stephanie's Glade) 24x86(95).

'Splendens' Occasional? Nymans (North Park, Pinetum end) 27x77(96); Petworth Park (park below Upperton) 23x**87**(97).

Q. dalechampii At Lorien (hybrid?): 8x20(94).

Daimyo Oak *Q. dentata* Occasional in big gardens. West Dean Gardens (Wild Garden) 9x36(97).

Q. dilatata At Borde Hill (Gores Wood, p1936): **16x28**(95).

Q. ellipsoidalis Rare. Borde Hill (Stonepit Wood) 17x34(95).

Q. faginea At Borde Hill (Stonepit Wood): 11x30(95).

var. *tlemcenensis* Rare. West Dean Gardens (West Lawn, ?) 13x51(97).

Spanish Oak *Q. falcata* Rare. Warnham Court (Wild Garden) 21x50(97); Leonardslee (Cox's Walk by Dell) 19x50(96).

Hungarian Oak *Q. frainetto* Occasional; becoming widespread as young tree. Buxted Park (Trout Pool) 29x**174**(94); Brook House (NE field) 22x146, 23x119(93); Warnham Court (Wild Garden) 28x133(97); Dunnings Rd, East Grinstead 19x127, 25x97(97); Wakehurst Place (Entrance Grounds) 23x125(97); Hotham Park 25x91(97).

Q. glandulifera Rare. Borde Hill (Little Bentley Wood) 13x22(95); Fontridge Manor (farm muckheap) 8x26(94).

Q. glauca At Wakehurst Place (Slips): 11x34++(97).

Q. x heterophylla Rare. Wakehurst Place (below Pinetum) 12x33(97).

Q. x hickelii At Borde Hill (Stonepit Wood): 10x**31**(95).

Q. x hispanica 'Heterophylla' Rare. Hollycombe (garden) 19x70(97); Hotham Park (E) 15x59(97).

Lucombe Oak 'Lucombeana' Occasional. St Roche's Arboretum (N side, fine slender tree) 33x109(97); Red Oaks (low pollard) 22x230@0.8m(97); Beauport Park (12th/17th) 20x139@1.1m(92); Staplefield Place 25x125@1m(96).

Holm Oak *Q. ilex* Abundant. Ashburnham (Target) 26x105@1.2m(93); Bishop's Palace (hollow) 15x142@1m(97); Rocks Park School 17x160@0.5m(94).

'Gramuntia' At Borde Hill (Azalea Ring, p1912): 10x47(95).

Bear Oak *Q. ilicifolia* At Borde Hill (Stonepit Wood/lake, ?): 9x19(95).

Shingle Oak *Q. imbricaria* Occasional. Sedgewick Park (park by drive) 22x**88**(97); Borde Hill (opposite drive entrance) 19x57(95); Wakehurst Place (Slips/Pinetum) 12x68@1.2m(97).

Californian Black Oak *Q. kelloggii* Rare. Borde Hill (S of Stonepit Wood) 19x59 and (?) 17x69(95); Nymans (Wild Garden) 16x41(96).

Laurel Oak *Q. laurifolia* At West Dean Gardens (Wild Garden - x *schochiana*?) 7x22(97).

Lea's Oak *Q. x leana* Rare. Hollycombe (garden, fine tree) 21x**83**(97); Borde Hill (Stonepit Wood) 18x32(95).

Lebanon Oak *Q. libani* Rare. Borde Hill (E of Stonepit Wood) 17x42, 16x50(95); Knockbridge House 14x42.

'Angustifolia' At Borde Hill (Peartree Wood): 19x45(95).

Ludwig's Oak *Q. x ludoviciana* Rare. Borde Hill (Stonepit Wood) 22x47(95).

Caucasian Oak *Q. macranthera* Occasional. Borde Hill (head of lake) 17x63@1.2m(95); St Helens Woods (Hillside Road gate, best in 1965 group) 11x40(93).

Q. mas At Lorien (?): **12x32**(94).

Q. michauxii x robur At Lorien (?): 9x15(94).

Q. x moreha At Borde Hill (Stonepit Wood, p1936): **13**x30(95).

Bamboo-leaved Oak *Q. myrsinifolia* Occasional, in big gardens. Borde Hill (Gores Wood) **15**x39@0.3m(95); Wakehurst Place (Westwood Valley) 12x37++(97); South Lodge Hotel (towards lake) 8x**53**@0.8m+(96).

Water Oak *Q. nigra* Rare. Peasmarsh Place (p 1976) 9x20(94).

Q. nigra x phellos At Borde Hill (Stonepit Wood): 7x23(95).

Q. oxyodon Rare. High Beeches (below Pond, p1960) 6x20++(97).

Pin Oak *Q. palustris* Frequent: parks and big gardens. Cowdray Park: towards Lodsworth 27x105, Golf Course depot 22x88(97); Borde Hill (Naldred Farmhouse, fine tree) 22x88(95).

Sessile Oak *Q. petraea* Native; abundant on acid soils. Cowdray Park: in Oaters Wood 37x104, Queen Elizabeth Oak (SU913226) 8x**389**@1.8m, house drive (with basal burr 3.1m wide, filled with concrete) 30x226@2.3m(97); Beauport Park (estate road) 34x194(97); The Mens ('Idehurst Oak') 26x193@1.2m(97); Plaistow village green 23x169(97); Ashburnham (Milestone Toll) 35x140(94); Stanmer Park (by A27) 31x135(93); Leonardslee (carpark) 25x193@1m(96); and see 'Big Trees'.

'Mespiliifolia' Rare. Wakehurst Place (house drive) 18x92@0.8m(97); Hotham Park (mid) 16x87(97).

The king of trees

The English **oak** - Kipling's 'Sussex weed' - is by far the most important tree in the county's landscape and ecology. Oak collections or Querceta, containing a huge range of exotic species, are also a feature of several parks and gardens.

If the oak is the king of trees, then the king of oaks is surely the Hungarian oak (*Quercus frainetto*) with its sumptuous, elaborately-lobed leaves and characteristic cartwheel of radiating grey boughs. And the king of Hungarian oaks, both for stature and perfect growth, is appropriately a Sussex tree, growing just above the trout pool in Buxted Park (p. 1), where it was first spotted by Alan Mitchell on a cold, wet afternoon in 1991. It can be seen from the footpath on the other side of the pool, and no tree in Sussex is better worth a visit.

Another remarkable tree is the chestnut-leaved oak (*Q. castaneifolia*) at Beauport Park, which holds court in a hidden corner of the woods more than a kilometre from the house. Elwes and Henry visited it in 1910, when it was 11x46. In 1977 it was x139, and, like the even bigger tree at Kew, it continues to grow unabated.

The sessile oak is one of the few really memorable native trees which is still hardly ever planted. The Weald is one of its strongholds, and in many woods on lighter soils most of the oaks are this large-leaved, smooth-boled species, but 99 trees out of 100 ever planted are English oak instead. The English oak is also much better at colonising new sites, so that sessile oak is very much characteristic of ancient woodlands and old parks. At Cowdray, all the medieval pollards are sessile, but next door at Petworth, Capability Brown planted English oak. Even on the clay of the Low Weald, which is the English oak's heartland, trees of exceptional form or vigour, such as the spendid tree on Plaistow green, tend to be sessile.

Queen Elizabeth is said to have detoured at Cowdray to see the giant tree (front cover) which now bears her name. The legend, like most, is picturesque but apocryphal: the Queen Elizabeth Oak could not have approached its current stature 400 years ago, whilst other oaks, now mere shells or else long collapsed, were presumably bigger then. Among today's sessile oaks, however, the Queen Elizabeth Oak is only rivalled in girth by the Pontfadog Oak near Chirk, whose taped measurements inflate its true size because of burrs and irregularities. In fact, the only reasonably clean-boled tree in Britain, of any kind, known to equal the Cowdray tree is the famous English oak at Bowthorpe Farm in Lincolnshire: its girth is identical (to within one per cent) and its state of decay is about the same, with a wide gap on one side of the trunk.

Although it grows by a footpath in a picturesque corner of Sussex, the Queen Elizabeth Oak is far less well-known than many a weedier tree, such as the Major or Knightwood Oaks. Its first known measurement dates from 1940, when it was 38' round. In 1967, Alan Mitchell measured it at 39', and, after another 30 years, it is now 40' in girth at the narrowest point (just above head-height). The steady growth suggested by these records implies an age of something over 1000 years, but it is reasonable to assume that the tree is somewhat younger than this: the widening gap on the south-east side of the trunk must subtract from the measured increment of the living part; the older measurements may not have been made at the narrowest point (the tree is now over 43' round at waist-height); and all trees, even when subjected to pollarding, tend to grow faster when young.

The Queen Elizabeth Oak is the perfect image of what an ancient oak in an ancient park ought to look like - squat, barrel-chested and clinging cheerfully onto life, with a few blasted limbs and a hollow heart the size of a kitchen and open to the sky; a home to little owls and beetles; almost a Walt Disney tree. Younger sessile oaks are quite different: clean-limbed, with heraldically magnificent vaults of branches. The great tree at Beauport Park is of this kind, and stood undamaged in 1987 in the midst of a wreckage of toppled beeches.

Another Queen Elizabeth Oak - this time an English oak - on Northiam village green was 12x227 in 1984. The Queen is said to have dined in its shade in August 1573, during a journey to Rye, and changed her green damask shoes. The shoes are still in the possession of the Frewen family of Brickwall, having outlasted the oak, which succumbed peacefully in 1991. However, the original tree was reported by the Gentleman's Magazine to have been largely destroyed by a storm in 1816, so it is possible that the legend had, over course of time, been grafted onto a young pretender. The Queen Elizabeth Oak mark three is already in its prime (20x151 in 1994), whilst marks four and five (sessile) are growing happily.

The most impressive - and probably the oldest - English oak in Sussex grows on the lawn at Whiligh, near Wadhurst (p.43). A manorial map of 1493 includes a picture of 'ye olde oak', apparently where the tree now stands, and it is mentioned in property deeds of the following year. 'When I was a child,' Lord Courthope, the owner of Whiligh, wrote in 1947, 'there was an opening over 2 feet wide into the hollow trunk, in which several persons could sit. The opening is now only a few inches wide.' The garden at Whiligh is opened one or two days each year under the National Gardens Scheme.

Repairs to the sessile oak roof of Westminster Hall were made in 1922 using timber from two oaks on the Whiligh estate; the Clerk of Works is said to have counted over 500 annual rings in one heartwood beam. More were used in 1948. In 1914, Lord Courthope had been offered the huge sum of £317 for a 634 cubic foot log - quite straight for 13m - from an English oak growing below the house. However, as he recalled in 1947, 'the haulage of so great a log would have destroyed three-quarters of a mile of farm road and half a mile of carriage drive; so the tree still stands.'

Its trunk diameter was 135cm in 1920 and 146cm in 1947, and it was 27x167 in 1994, suggesting an age now of about 350 years. A sessile oak, on the footpath behind Little Whiligh, is almost as fine and even bigger at 27x172.

Hybrids and intergrades between the two native species (*Q. x rosacea*) are probably not rare. Several of the Petworth oaks show intermediate features, while the gigantic leaves of the tree near the rose garden in Alexandra Park may be evidence of first-generation 'hybrid vigour'.

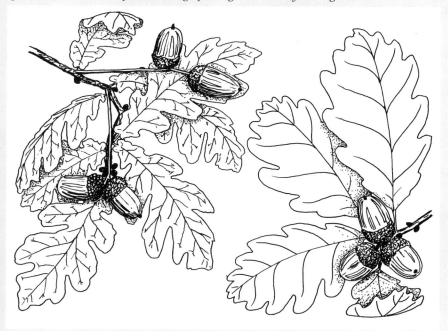

OAKS

Willow Oak *Q. phellos* Occasional. Borde Hill (opposite garden entrance) 16x46(95); Alexandra Park (model railway, pollard) x75(93).

Q. phillyreoides Rare. High Beeches (below Queen Mary's Walk) 10x16+15(94); Wakehurst Place (Entrance Grounds) 8x38@0.2m(97).

Basket Oak *Q. prinus* Rare. Borde Hill (Stonepit Wood) 13x27(95).

Downy Oak *Q. pubescens* Rare. Alexandra Park (top of oak bank) 20x92(93); Borde Hill (Gores Wood) 17x44(95).

Q. 'Pyrami' At Lorien (?): 12x25(94).

Pyrenean Oak *Q. pyrenaica* Rare. Borde Hill (outside Great Bentley Wood, p1913) 17x70(95).

Q. pyrenaica x robur Rare. Little Fontridge 10x25(94).

English Oak

English Oak *Q. robur* Native; abundant. Ashburnham: Burrage Wood 35x110, park below Steven's Crouch 15x245(94); Whiligh 10x285@1m(96); Danny (drive) 14x315@ground/1m, and 24x235(97); Knepp Castle ('Castle Oak') 25x207(96); Goodwood (icehouse; spread of 39m with four limbs resting on the ground) 23x218(97); Parham (near dovecote) 26x224(97); Eridge Park (White Hill) 27x244(94); and see 'Big Trees'.

'Atropurpurea' Rare. Leonardslee (below Dell) 7x25@1m(96).

• *The cypress oak is as slender as a Lombardy poplar, for which it is often mistaken*

Cypress Oak f. *fastigiata* Occasional; more frequent as a young municipal tree. St Roche's Arboretum (valley path, mid; wild tree?) 29x78(97); Beauport Park (Hollow Wood, wild tree?) 18x83@1.2m(97); Chelwood Beacon (in field, TQ428287, wild? but very slender) 17x36(94); Borde Hill (Naldred farmyard) 20x55(95).

'Filicifolia' At Hotham Park (mid): 14x38(97).

'Heterophylla' At Wakehurst Place (house drive): 5x27@1m(97).

'Purpurascens' At Lorien: 9x30(94).

Hybrid English Oak *Q. x rosacea* Native; probably frequent. Petworth Park (park outside Pleasure Grounds) 26x**222**(97); Alexandra Park (near top of steps opposite rose garden) 24x119(93).

Red Oak

Red Oak *Q. rubra* Abundant. Cowdray Park: garden 30x145, house drive 28x152(97); Horsham church (very fine) 23x172(98); Milton Mount Gardens (very stocky) 18x164@1m(97); Warnham church 20x133(93); Milland church 27x137@0.8m(97).

Q. x schochiana Rare. Borde Hill (Little Bentley Wood, N) 12x17(95); Little Fontridge 10x44@0.3m(94).

Shumard Oak *Q. shumardii* At Borde Hill (Gores Wood, p1936): 12x15(95).

Q. spathulata At Borde Hill (Gores Wood): 12x25(95).

Cork Oak *Q. suber* Occasional. Borde Hill (top of Stonepit Wood, Algerian seed 1922) 18x52(95); Ashburnham (drive by house) 13x109@1m(93); Goodwood (house front, notable 18th century planting) 11x100(97); West Stoke church 11x65(97); Slindon church 9x75@0.5m(97); Arundel Castle (behind church) 12x82(97).

Macedonian Oak *Q. trojana* Occasional. Borde Hill (E of Stonepit Wood) 16x56(95); Wakehurst Place (mansion lawn) 16x56++(97); Leonardslee (below Dell) 13x38(96).

Turner's Oak *Q. x turneri* Occasional. Borde Hill (North Park) 14x62 and 14x61(95); Warnham Court (Wild Garden) 15x87@0.5m(97); Alexandra Park (oak bank) 13x41(93).

Chinese Cork Oak *Q. variabilis* Rare. Hollycombe (gardens) 19x55(97); Borde Hill (Stonepit Wood) 18x51 and 15x48(95).

Black Oak *Q. velutina* Occasional. Wakehurst Place (above Pinetum) 20x84(97); Borde Hill (S of Stonepit Wood) 20x80(95); Knepp Castle (Pleasure Grounds) 16x76(96).

var. *missouriensis* At Borde Hill (start of Stephanie's Glade): 20x49(96).

'Rubrifolia' At Tilgate Park (mid S): **26**x81(96).

Q. warburgii Rare. Petworth Park (cottage below Pleasure Grounds) 20x**84**(97); Borde Hill (Stonepit Wood, p1938) 11x23(95).

Q. wislizenii Rare. High Beeches (top) **13**x48(94); Borde Hill (Lullings Ghyll) 9x45@0.4m(95).

BUCKTHORN

Buckthorn *Rhamnus catharticus* Native; frequent on chalk. Ashcombe Bottom 8x32@0.1m+(95).

Rhododendron arboreum Occasional in large gardens. Rivendell 11x45; Tilgate Forest Lodge 8x47(96).

R. arboreum x thompsonii At Leonardslee (Loderi Garden): 11x43@0.4m(96).

Rhus potaninii Rare. Borde Hill (Stonepit Wood, p1940) 13x32, 10x34@1.2m(95).

R. x pulvinata At Nymans (Top Garden, suckers from old tree) 8x16(96).

Chinese Varnish Tree *R. verniciflua* Rare. Snape House 14x35.

LOCUST TREES

Robinia x ambigua 'Bella Rosea' Rare. Stanmer Park (Arboretum, p1964) 8x12(95); Borde Hill (Stephanie's Glade, recumbent) 6x20(95).

'Decaisneana' Rare. Borde Hill (Garden of Allah) 21x79(95).

R. hartwigii At Borde Hill (Stephanie's Glade): **16x41**@1m(95).

R. x holdtii 'Britzensis' At Borde Hill (Stephanie's Glade): 15x44(95).

R. kelseyi At Borde Hill (Stephanie's Glade): **18**x44(95).

False Acacia *R. pseudacacia* Abundant and naturalised. Ashburnham (Ironspring campsite) 23x94(93); Oaklands House (short straight bole; dying back) 17x174@1m(93).

• *False acacia wood is superbly durable, but the tree is too crooked to be worth cropping*

'Aurea' At the Sheep House: 14x40.

'Bessoniana' Rare? Stanmer Park (Arboretum, p1964) **18**x22(94); Vallence Road, Lewes (?) 17x**50**(96).

Golden Robinia 'Frisia' Abundant in small gardens. Clermont Road, Brighton 15x39(94); Jubilee Gardens, Chichester 14x30(97).

'Monophylla' Rare. St Cuthman's School (bridlepath N of school) 22x70(97).

'Rehderi' At Warnham Court (Nursery House paddock): 8x27@1m+(97).

'Rozynskyana' Rare. Nymans (North Park) 21x**64**+(96).

'Semperflorens' At Nymans (North Park): **21x40**+31(96).

'Tortuosa' Rare. Fair Oak 7x23@0.5m(97); Warnham Court (Wild Garden, recumbent) 4x31(97).

Clammy Locust *R. viscosa* Rare. Borde Hill (carpark) **14**x51(95).

White Willow *Salix alba* Native; frequent near water, principally in the east. Pond Wood 24x107(94); Amberley Wild Brooks (below village) 10x**238**@1-1.7m(97); Litlington (lane near Knowle Cottage) 23x156(94).

Coral-bark Willow 'Britzensis'/'Chermesina' Frequent: belts and small gardens. Alexandra Park (filter beds bank) **23**x51(93); Charleston Manor 22x**83**(94); Great Wigsell (coppice) 20x**129**@0.1m(94); De La Warr Rd, Bexhill 12x61(94).

Bat Willow var. *caerulea* Occasional; mostly in the lower E. Rother. St Helens Woods (Bill Vint Meadow, broken) x107(94).

Silver Willow var. *sericea* Occasional, mostly in small gardens. Wickham Farm (track) 19x64(96); Brighton Rd roundabout, Crawley 15x64(96).

Golden Willow var. *vitellina* Occasional? Reach Wood 14x28++(96); Banks Farm 10x34(95).

Chinese Weeping Willow *S. babylonica* At Wakehurst Place (Slips, K. Rushforth collection): 7x23(97).

Corkscrew Willow 'Tortuosa' Now abundant in small gardens. Slugwash Gardens 13x32(91); Little Fontridge 11x58@0.7m(94).

Common Sallow *S. caprea* Native; abundant. Darwell Wood (TQ700204, long straight bole) 20x36(94); Baldwins Farm (field, TQ718207) 10x83@1.2m(93).

Grey Sallow *S. cinerea* subsp. *oleifolia* Native; abundant. Powdermill Wood, Catsfield (in Powdermill Trust reserve, TQ733146) **13**x48@0.7m(95); Dumpford Park Farm (SU825217) 10x46(97).

S. x ehrhartiana At Steyning recreation ground (?): 11x42@1m(96).

Crack Willow *S. fragilis* Native; abundant. Loxwood (bed of Wey and Arun canal, TQ034312) 23x104(97); Wadhurst Park (near Combe Manor, TQ626283) 11x138(94); Greatham Bridge (Wey and Arun canal bank) 14x134(97).

Basford Willow *S. x rubens* f. *basfordiana* Rare. Alexandra Park (Coronation Wood, p1937) **19**m(94), 17x62@0.9m(82).

Weeping Willow. *S. x sepulcralis* 'Chrysocoma' Abundant in small gardens. Charleston Manor 17x76(94); Alexandra Park (downstream from bandstand) 13x83(93).

Salamon's Weeping Willow 'Salamonii' Rare. Alexandra Park (below bandstand) 13x49(93).

S. x sericans Native; occasional. Banks Farm (planted) 11x35+(94).

Almond Willow *S. triandra* Native; rather rare. Sheffield Park (Reservoir Pond) 7x49@0.2m(94).

Common Osier *S. viminalis* Native; frequent on wet ground. Hampden Park (SW corner, young planted tree) 10x21@0.1m(95); Banks Farm (planted) 7x**32**@1m(95).

Elder *Sambucus nigra* Native; abundant but seldom tree-sized. Spring Gardens carpark 7x46@1.2m(94).

Sassafras *Sassafras albidum* Rare: large gardens. Cowdray Park (drive by house) 10x27(97).

Prince Albert's Yew *Saxegothaea conspicua* Rare. Nymans (Pinetum) 6x19(96).

Umbrella Tree *Sciadopitys verticillata* Occasional: large gardens. Tilgate Park (Pinetum, p1905) 15x57(96); Sheffield Park (N of Second Lake, p1911) 14x48(94).

Coast Redwood *Sequoia sempervirens* Frequent. Keeper's Farm 43x144, 39x179(97); Dangstein 31x194(97); Leonardslee (valley) 39x127(96); Wakehurst Place (Horsebridge Woods) 38x137(97); Milton Mount Gardens 25x179(97); Borden Wood 35x174(97); Fair Oak 35x171(97); Eridge Park (Pinetum, p1885) 28x180(94); Malt House (Pinetum) 38x153(97) - and see 'Tall Trees'.

'Adpressa' Rare. Broadbridge Heath (by B2199 at TQ151321) 13x36, 12x45(97); Wakehurst Place (Pinetum) 12x35(97).

'Glauca' Rare. Doma 9x18.

WILLOWS

• *The ancient white willow pollard below Amberley village has the biggest willow trunk in Britain*

• *Coral-bark willows in winter are like giant orange flames, a striking feature in the landscape*

ELDER

COAST REDWOOD

A home from home

Adapted as it is to the perpetual fogs and mild temperatures of the north Californian coasts, it is slightly surprising that the **coast redwood** will grow in Sussex, and astonishing that it does so well.

After a winter of easterly winds, mature trees can look practically dead, but will still outgrow most of the other Rocky Mountain conifers and have yet to begin to show the signs of old age.

A tree planted south of the Inn in Tilgate Park holds the record for building a columnar bole 1m thick (broader than a front door-frame) - 29 years.

Three of the tallest in England stand together in a field at Keeper's Farm near Milland, with only the surrounding greensand hills to shelter them.

WELLINGTONIA

Wellingtonia *Sequoiadendron giganteum* Frequent as old and very young tree. Nymans (long woodland walk, died back from 47m) 43x209(97); Cowdray Park (avenue, p1871) 30x310(97); Rocks Park School (behind school) 34x306(98) - and see 'Big Trees' and 'Tall Trees'.
Weeping Wellingtonia 'Pendulum' Rare. Wakehurst Place (Entrance Grounds) 15x35(97).

Mighty landmarks

The seed of the **wellingtonia** was first brought here from California in 1853: Veitch's nurseries sold the seedlings for two guineas a pair. Charles Lamb at Beauport Park bought several; two planted out in the shelter of Ring Wood in 1856 were 28x150 in 1908, 31x181 and 30x165 in 1931, 41x243 and 39x236 in 1981, and 41x258 and 39x254 in 1997.

Growth in height, then, is moderately rapid here but decelerates and stops at half that of the Californian 'big trees', thanks to exposure and lightning strikes. Growth in girth, at first phenomenal, then settles into a steady increment which, after 140 years, has made Wellingtonias the biggest trees in nearly every part of Britain, including Sussex.

The species plays a role in the landscape out of all proportion to its actual abundance. It is sensitive to sea air and likes plenty of humidity, but is extraordinarily indifferent to mere weather, with groups and lines standing tall and proud as a distant landmark on many inland ridges - at Bexleyhill Common, at Shernfold Park near Frant, at Scalands House above Robertsbridge, or at Chiddinglye where, on top of the Weald near West Hoathly, an avenue has spire-shaped crowns to 39m tall.

Curiously, the timber is scarcely stronger than cardboard and the tree depends on its sheer bulk; tops are often snapped or shattered. It thrives in clay or sand, but dislikes the very light soils which many conifers revel in, and hates chalk.

The only examples on the Downs which have yet notched up the Wealden commonplace of 2m in trunk diameter are far in the west at Singleton cemetery and the Stansted Park arboretum.

A tree at Rocks Park School in Uckfield (p. 4) - improbably located above the playground in a modern housing estate - and the end tree in the great avenue at Cowdray, are currently vying as the largest-boled wellingtonias in England, though, as they are all growing so fast, others may well have crept up on the wings.

Pagoda Tree *Sophora japonica* Occasional: parks and large gardens. Highbrook church 16x65(96); Hotham Park 14x70(97); The Oval 13x75@0.7m(93); Great Dixter (outside entrance) 10x46@0.8m(94).
'Pendula' At Nymans (house lawn): 5x22(96).
'Variegata' Rare. Stanmer Park (Arboretum, p1964) 10x28(95).

Bollwyller Pear X *Sorbopyrus auricularis* 'Malifolia' At Wakehurst Place (behind Specimen Beds): 9x30@1m+(97).

ROWANS & WHITEBEAMS

Sorbus alnifolia Rare. Nymans (North Park) 13x49(96); Borde Hill (below lake) 12x**57**@0.5m(95).
American Rowan *S. americana* Rare. Fontridge Manor 9x20.
Whitebeam *S. aria* Native. Abundantly planted; infrequent as a wild tree. Watergate Hanger (SU777119, several very slender stems) 22x35++(97); Hampden Park (behind tennis) 17x69(94); Fairmile Bottom (by steps up from carpark) 20x50++(97); Bignor Park (N garden, long bole) 21x40(97).
'Chrysophylla' At St Roche's Arboretum (lower entrance): 10x22(97).
'Lutescens' Abundant: streets and small gardens. Horsham Park (by leisure centre) 11x46(96).
'Majestica' And other large-leaved forms, frequent street trees. Warnham Court (Wild Garden) 12x48(97); Westergate (street planting) 9x51(97).
Rowan *S. aucuparia* Native: abundant and much planted. Duckyls Wood 19x56(96); Ashdown Forest Golf Course (above Tompset's Bank, TQ421333) 14x**60**@1m(94); Leonardslee (beyond Camellia Walk, decaying) 17x57(96).
Cut-leaved Rowan 'Aspleniifolia' Rare. Borde Hill (Gores Wood) **16x31**(95).
'Beissneri' Becoming frequent. Withdean Park (rose beds) 6x22(94).
'Xanthocarpa' At Borde Hill (Gores Wood): 7x20(96).
S. bristoliensis Rare. Hastings cemetery (Ivyhouse Lane fence, ?): **18x71**(93).
Japanese Rowan *S. commixta* Frequent amenity tree. Borde Hill (Pirates Adventure) 10x29(95); St Johns Meads church (p1958) 8x37@0.8m(94).
True Service *S. domestica* Denizen; rare. Borde Hill (S of Stephanie's Glade; var. *pyrifera*; huge crown much broken) 17x**86**(95).
S. 'Embley' Frequent street tree. William Parker School 11x25(93).
S. esserteauiana Rare: large gardens. Leonardslee (below Camellia Walk) 14x33(96); St Helens Wood (Hillside Road gate, ?, p1965) 13x**35**(93).
'Flava' Rare. Borde Hill (Gores Wood) **13x23**(95); Highdown 8x16(97).
S. folgneri Rare. Borde Hill (Gores Wood, p1937) 13x23@1m(95).
Hupeh Rowan *S. hupehensis* Occasional - large gardens. Borde Hill (Garden of Allah) 14x39, 13x**52**@1.1m(95); Tilgate Park (outside walled garden, very fine) 12x41(97).
S. hybrida Rare. Borde Hill (Gores Wood) 8x26(96).
S. insignis At Borde Hill (Gores Wood, ?): 11x19(95).
Swedish Whitebeam *S. intermedia* Abundant in streets and parks. Malt House (Pinetum) **20**x74@1.2m, 19x71(97); Hollycombe (railway) 15x78@1m(97); Garland Square, Tangmere 11x66(97); The Green, Southwick 15x67(94); Hotham Park 14x68(97).
S. japonica At Wakehurst Place (E of Mansion Pond): **7x28**(97).
S. 'Joseph Rock' Occasional. Leonardslee (below Camellia Walk) 9x17(96); Sheffield Park (below entrance) 8x18(94).

● *Rowan trees were once planted beside a house to ward off witches*

● *The true service was proved to be a British native only in 1983, when a dozen trees probably over a thousand years old were spotted on cliffs near Cardiff*

Fontainbleau Service *S. latifolia* Occasional. Gravetye Forest (N bank of lake) 13x40(97); Borde Hill (below carpark, 20m spread, p1907) 12x93(96).

S. mougeotii Rare. Highdown **14**x32(97).

S. pallescens Rare. Borde Hill (Gores Wood) 16x51, 16x42(95); Wakehurst Place (above Pinetum) 11x81@0.2m(97).

S. pohuashanensis Rare. Borde Hill (Gores Wood) **16**x36(95); Stanmer Park (Arboretum, p1964) 9x25(95).

S. randaiensis At Borde Hill (Gores Wood, p1938): **16x23**(95).

Sargent's Rowan *S. sargentiana* Occasional in big gardens. Newtimber Old Rectory (dying back) 6x21@1.2m(97).

Ladder-leaf Rowan *S. scalaris* Occasional in big gardens. Borde Hill (Gores Wood) 12x36@0.9m, 10x**54**@0.4m(95); Goffs Park 5x15(97).

S. 'Theophrasta' At Highdown (Chalk Garden, ?): **13**x46(97).

S. thibetica At Wakehurst Place (Slips, Kingdon-Ward collection): 13x29, 10x32 and 12x26(97).

'John Mitchell' Occasional as young garden tree. Alexandra Park (above Shornden playground) **17x55**(93).

Bastard Service *S. x thuringiaca* 'Fastigiata' Occasional as a street tree. Lorien 10x25@1.3m(94).

Wild Service *S. torminalis* Native; frequent on heavy soils and now much planted. Petworth Park: park carpark (crowded tree) 23x39@1.2m, below Upper Pond dam (with a good bole) 16x104(97); Parsonage Farm (short slanted bole) 16x**139**@0.9m(94); Darwell Wood (TQ697703, good bole) 15x90(94); Ashburnham (Target; closely resembles Parsonage Farm tree) 16x106@0.6m(93); Cowdray Park (Moor Farm field by A272, good bole) 17x89(97); Lye's Farm (TQ304218; divides low) 15x92@1m(96); Farney Close School 17x80(94).

• *The 'John Mitchell' whitebeam has round leaves like saucers, silver beneath. The single 'original' at Westonbirt arboretum has helped popularise the form in recent years, but the mysterious tree in Alexandra Park appears to be its twin*

Udimore's venerable celebrity

*Standing in the clay of the Low Weald, you are unlikely to be far from a **wild service**, but this tree is often overlooked and often unrecognised. It is unsociable, and thus numerically uncommon: a grove of twenty by the Napier road junction with Queensway in St Leonards is a remarkable sight, especially when the whole wood is in blossom.*

Local campaigning saved this group when Queensway was planned to run straight through it in 1977 but, as I write, it is again threatened by the proposed Hastings bypass.

The national champion wild service, at Parsonage Farm in Udimore (p. 21), is something of a superstar in the tree world. It can be seen from the B2089 and, with its huge, low spread, is a most distinguished record-holder. Its girth was recorded by Alexander Howard in 1947 as 'nearly 11 feet', implying an age now of around 170 years. Its nearest rivals in the county grow on the greensand at Cowdray and Petworth, although the tree is naturally very rare on this soil.

Recently, the wild service's role as an indicator of the oldest and least disturbed of woods and hedge-lines has perhaps been undermined by indiscriminate plantings. Sixty were planted at Ripe in the jubilee year of 1977.

Himalayan Whitebeam *S. vestita* Occasional: recent municipal plantings. Borde Hill (Pirates Adventure, p1907) 17x**90**(95).

Vilmorin's Rowan *S. vilmoriniana* Occasional: large and some small gardens. Borde Hill (Gores Wood) 11x14(95); Warnham Court (Wild Garden) 5x25(97); Chelwood Vachery 7x41@0.3m(94).

S. 'Wilfrid Fox' Rare? Fontridge Manor 9x30@0.2m(94); Lancaster Grange 8x38(97).

Stuartia monadelpha Occasional in big gardens. High Beeches (below pond, beautiful tree) **11x24**(93); Borde Hill (Gores Wood) 10x18(96); South Lodge Hotel (far W) 8x18(96).

S. pseudocamellia Occasional in big gardens. Tilgate Forest Lodge 11x25+22(96); Leonardslee (below Cross Paths) 9x33@0.4m(96).

S. serrata Rare: Borde Hill (Gores Wood) **9**x18(96); Nymans (Walled Garden) 8x19(96).

S. sinensis Occasional in big gardens. Tilgate Park 14x**38**(96); Wakehurst Place (Specimen Beds) 10x46@0.2m(97); Borde Hill (old Kitchen Garden wall, p1914) 12x42@0.5m(95).

Royal sap

*If there was ever a tree with blue sap, it must be **Stuartia sinensis**.*

Expensive, slow and demanding, this is exclusively a tree of the big gardens in the High Weald, where the specimen above the Slips at Wakehurst Place attracts so much attention from visitors that its root-run has had to be cordoned off.

The bark is flesh-coloured, perfectly smooth and as cold as marble; the dainty crown is

studded with white camellia-flowers in July; the elegant foliage comes alight in autumn.

Perhaps the best example of all is in Tilgate Park, on the lawn north-west of the Peace Garden. Tilgate is now a public park, so the stuartia suffers the annual indignity of hearts and initials carved into its exquisite bark. In autumn, however, the outer skin darkens and peels like tissue paper, revealing a bone-white undersurface: and, amazingly, nearly all evidence of the season's accumulation of tattoos is sloughed off with it.

Hemsley's Storax *S. hemsleyana* Rare. Nymans (Walled Garden) 10x**36**+(96); High Beeches (below pond, p1914; lovely tree) 10x28(97); Forest Ridge 7x27(90).

Snowbell Tree *S. japonica* Occasional; larger gardens. Heaselands 9x14+13(96); Borde Hill (Gores Wood) 6x33@1m(95).

'Fargesii' At Nymans (Top Garden): 7x27, 6x28(96).

Big-leaved Storax *S. obassia* Rare. Nymans (Walled Garden) 7x29@1.2m(96).

Sycopsis sinensis Rare. Wakehurst Place (Slips, dying back): **10x19**+18(97); Alexandra Park (herbacious beds bridge) 6x23@0.1m(98).

Symplocos paniculata At Wakehurst Place (above Slips) 6x17(98).

Tree Lilac *Syringa reticulata* At Stanmer Park (Arboretum): **9x22**+(94).

Taiwanese Coffin Tree *Taiwania cryptomerioides* Rare. Wakehurst Place (head of Westwood Valley) 8x16(97).

Pond Cypress *Taxodium ascendens* Occasional; collections. Knepp Castle (cedar avenue) 18x**68**(96); Beauport Park: Hotel drive (snapped off) 13x53(92); 10th hole (leans) 17x45(97); Sheffield Park: N of First Lake (snapped off) 7x46, estate cottages 15x48(94).
Swamp Cypress *Taxodium distichum* Frequent: parks and gardens. Alexandra Park (Shornden valley) 29x89(93); Danny 14x116@1.2m(97); Railwayland, Lewes (seven boles) 18x131@0.5m(94).
'Pendens' At Alexandra Park (Shornden Valley): **24x58**(94).

YEWS

English Yew *Taxus baccata* Native; Abundant everywhere. Ashburnham (Target, sprouty) 25m (93); Close Walks 25x99(80; survives but dying back; outstanding long clean bole); Coldwaltham Church 14x296(97); and see 'Big Trees'.
'Adpressa' Rare. Alexandra Park (below Buckshole) 9x**66**(93).
Golden Yew f. *aurea* Frequent in old shrubberies. Warnham Court (Wild Garden) 10x28(97); Ely Grange (rockery) 9x31(94).
Irish Yew 'Fastigiata' Frequent, especially in churchyards. Beauport Park (behind 13th tee) 14x**118**@0.7m(97).
'Fructu Luteo' At Highdown (Chalk Garden): 7x25++(97).
Japanese Yew *Taxus cuspidata* Rare: collections. Borde Hill (Warren Wood) **11x48**(96).

Spur-leaf *Tetracentron sinense* At Nymans (Top Garden, dying back): 13x44@0.3m(96).

Euodia *Tetradium daniellii* Occasional: collections. Stanmer Park (Arboretum, SE edge, p1964) 10x31(94); West Dean Gardens (Spring Garden) 7x37@1.2m(97); Highdown (Lower Garden, seed 1929) 9x31(97).

ARBOR-VITAE

• *The eastern white cedar was probably the first tree to be brought back from the New World, in 1536. But it neither grows big nor lives long here*

Eastern White Cedar *Thuja occidentalis* Occasional (semi-dwarf forms such as 'Rheingold' are abundant). Barham House (huge bush) 9m(94); Sedlescombe church (recumbent) 5x32(93).
'Ellwangeriana Aurea' Rare. Broadfield Park 6x20++(97); Snell Hatch Cemetery 5x22@1m(97).
'Fastigiata' At Riccard's Cottage (?): 7x18@1.2m(94).
'Lutea' Rare. Broadfield Park 9x46@0.5m(97).
'Spiralis' Occasional in small gardens. Snell Hatch Cemetery 11x32@0.9m, 9x**36**@1m(97).
Chinese Thuja *T. orientalis* Occasional - notably in country churchyards. Ewhurst church 10x51@1m(94); Bury church 10x59@0.1m(97); Wivelsfield church 7x50@ground(94); Old Heathfield church 8x44@0.1m(94); Udimore church 8x32(94).
'Elegantissima' Frequent - a rock-garden conifer. Church Street, Crawley (churchyard) 6x19++(97); Woodmancote church 6x16++(97).
'Flagelliformis' At Lydhurst: 9x36@0.6m, 10x25@0.2m(80).
Western Red Cedar *T. plicata* Abundant - parks, plantations and hedges. St Roche's Arboretum (S track, forks) 35x133(97); Handcross Park (woods) 30x134(98); Malt House (Pinetum, vigorous) 35x108(97); Stonehurst (valley, forks) 34x129@1m(97).
'Pyramidalis' Occasional: hedges etc. Alexandra Park (above boating lake) 18x52(96).
'Semperaurescens' Rare? Leonardslee (beyond Camellia Walk) 14x43(96).
'Wintergold' Rare. Snell Hatch Cemetery (?) 9x19++(97).
Golden Thuja 'Zebrina' An abundant garden tree. Nymans (Top Garden) 20x84(96); Tilgate Park (Pinetum, p1905) 20x74(96).
T. plicata x standishii At Wakehurst Place: Pinetum, **9x26**(97).
Japanese Thuja *T. standishii* Occasional in large gardens. Leonardslee (Hill Garden) 19x66(96); Eridge Park (Pinetum; forest of layered stems) 17x93@1.8m++(94); Alexandra Park: behind Pumping Station 16x57, Bohemia gate 17x50(93).

Hiba *Thujopsis dolabrata* Frequent in small and large gardens. Leonardslee (below Mossy Ghyll) 17x40(96); Ashburnham (Target) 12x53(93).
'Variegata' Occasional; reverts. Duckyls Wood 14x22++(97); Normanhurst (estate road) 10x26(93).
var. *hondai* At Stanmer Park (Arboretum, p1964): 6x20(94).

LIMES

American Lime *Tilia americana* Occasional; several recent municipal plantings. Hampden Park: W edge 23x70, by lake (cut back) x71(94); Alexandra Park (bank above bowling green, grafted at 1.4m) 19x**99**(94).
var. *vestita* Rare. Nymans (bottom of North Park, fine slender tree) **24x66**(97).
T. chinensis Rare. Borde Hill (Stephanie's Glade, ?) 10x19(96).
Small-leaved Lime *T. cordata* A rare native in the Weald; now abundantly planted. Stansted Park (track N of entrance) 28x99(97); Worth Way, Worth (200m east of church, N side) 23x**252**(93).

Sentinel of the churchyard

Yews have a scattered distribution in woods on light soils throughout the county; there are a few pure stands which have developed on the western Downs, notably at Kingley Vale and Telegraph House. They are also abundant in Victorian shrubberies. But it is as a churchyard tree that the yew is most celebrated.

There are some 37 "ancient" yews in Sussex churchyards, which it is reasonable to imagine are at least 500 years old; most churchyards can also boast one or more younger trees. Very few have a known planting date: the fine tree at Sutton (14x129@1m in 1997) was planted, according to an anonymous correspondent in Vaughan Cornish's The Churchyard Yew and Immortality, in 1670, but looks younger (it is growing in a good site for a yew). On rather less suitable clay at Lurgashall, a yew planted by W. H. Yaldwyn on his 21st birthday in September, 1821 is now 16x101@0.3m.

The age of the biggest churchyard yews is a tantalising enigma which will probably never be answered satisfactorily. Growth-rings cannot be counted, because all these trees are very hollow. Historic measurements, which ought to provide us with a rate of increment in size, can seldom be relied upon because yew boles are generally sprouty and irregular and it takes an experienced eye to thread the tape-measure around the narrowest route.

The largest of the county's yews, at Coldwaltham church, has a relatively straight, columnular bole which is swollen at the base but only produces small sprouts to struggle with (p. 16). Successive measurers have recorded it as x303cm (1896), x300cm (1961) and x296cm (1997). This represents an increase in accuracy but can hardly mask any significant growth.

The next largest, at Crowhurst, has been measured regularly since 1680, when John Aubrey recorded a diameter of 262cm. The more recent - and probably more accurate - measurements tell of steady growth, exaggerated in the last few decades as the southern part of the bole has sagged outwards: x257cm in 1879, x259cm in 1894, x264cm in 1954, x270cm in 1965, and x289cm in 1998. The timber of yew is so fluid that the gap, which must have yawned open in the rest of the bole as the southern section split away, is now hardly visible: in another hundred years the leaning part will probably have been shed, and the enigma will remain of a perfectly clean bole the same size as, or slightly smaller than, the tree measured four centuries earlier.

The most influential recent estimates of the ages of some of the very big yew trees have been those of Allen Meredith, who suggests that the Coldwaltham yew is much the oldest in Sussex and may be 3000 years old.

The two largest yews in the famous grove in

Kingley Vale are 15x178@0.5m and 15x175@0.5m. When J. C. Loudon visited this remote and eerie forest in 1829, the largest he measured were x90cm, with their ages then being estimated at 200 years. It all seems to fit together perfectly, and to make these trees now about 350 years old. However, it could well be that Loudon's trees were some of the smaller ones, and that the biggest are rather older - 500 years seems to be the generally accepted estimate. What is certain is that, full of presence as the yew grove is, none of the trees are more than slightly hollow and none convey anything like the sense of extreme, patient antiquity of the largest churchyard specimens.

The biggest and oldest yew found in Sussex which is not connected with a holy site is by a hollow lane behind the farm stables at Barlavington, under the scarp of the downs. A rather bushy, vigorous tree, which does not seem to be hollow, this is 15x248@0.1m(97), but the diameter, measured on the slope beneath masses of sprouts, rather exaggerates its true size. Allen Meredith, however, has estimated its age at as much as 1400 years.

A similar tree on the greensand scarp above Well Cottage, Hollycombe, is 14x234@0m(97) (with another stem from ground-level not included in the measurement). Roe deer have grazed the dense growth on its trunk into a kind of natural topiary. A yew with a bole like a towering gothic column, by the lane from Best Beech Hill south of Wadhurst down into Tidebrook, was 16x158 in 1994.

At Worth, the old yew - 10x165@0.3m on the clean bole in 1997 - stands just outside the churchyard boundary bank and may have been planted when Street House was built in the 16th century.

The planting of yews to shelter farmhouses (or possibly to commemorate their construction) was a common practice: such trees are particularly abundant on the greensand in the west (where yews grow well) and

normally stand just south-west of the house. At Bradford's Farm, Little Horsted, the bole of the old yew practically touches the cottage's northern wall.

In the grounds of Seaford College a very old yew, which forks low down, is 16x206@0.4m. It stands about 70m west of East Lavington church and was probably originally within the holy site.

Considering the age of our population of churchyard yews, the numbers of recent losses is perhaps a cause for concern. The deliberate felling of any of these ancient monuments - as happened at East Lavant in 1977/8 and at Bignor a few years earlier - is an inexcusable piece of arrogance. For the huge tree south of East Lavant church to survive storms, droughts and snowfalls for 1500 years at least, venerated by the Saxons and early Christians, only to be pronounced 'dangerous' by the head forester at Goodwood because it was hollow and to be cut down, was a lamentable fate indeed. The two larger yews at Sullington have also been lost recently, while that at Aldingbourne stands dead. Other losses of notable trees have been at South Bersted and Whatlington (after 1945) and at Hardham, where a tree resembling the Rotherfield yew lost its top in a storm of about 1820 and had long gone by the 1940s. Fortunately, interest in caring for those that remain has now been stimulated again.

At Ratton Manor, Willingdon, the yew trees known as 'The Twelve Apostles' are said to have been planted by the monks of Wilmington Priory, who set a curse upon anyone who should destroy them. The present line of trees probably dates from the eighteenth century, but the curse holds good. The laying low of the first three Apostles in the 1960s is said to have been followed almost immediately by the death, in turn, of the manager of the tree surgery business, of his foreman and of the owner of the trees: the remaining nine Apostles are now the subject of a preservation order.

Our largest churchyard yews

In some sort of descending order of seniority - judged in terms of decrepitude and presence as well as of dimensions - these are now the largest Sussex churchyard yews. N/S/E/W give the direction of the tree from the current church.

1 Coldwaltham 14x296(97) NW - growing on an apparently natural mound above Amberley Wild Brooks. The monumental trunk is very hollow, with a gap on the north side, and is filled up with humus almost to eye-level.

2 Crowhurst 12x289@0.8-1.5m(98) S. The railings were put up in 1907. Legend tells that King Harold's steward was hung from the tree after the Battle of Hastings for refusing to tell where the King's treasure was hidden.

3 Rotherfield 11x220(94) N. A slanting, broken fragment of a once gigantic bole.

4 Stedham 11x282@0m(97) SW - forming a hollow cup of branches which divide at 1m. The iron hoops that were intended to hold it together have recently been released.

5 Buxted 14x248@0.1m(94) N - very similar to the Stedham tree.

6 Northiam 10x201@0.3m(94) S. Three diverging fragments remain of a huge bole.

7 Lavant 9x216@0.8m NW. The tree lost many of its roots a few years ago when the church was extended; it was trimmed back and currently looks rather poorly. It is very hollow and the tape was run around an almost isolated fragment on the north side.

8 Tangmere 12x232(97) S. The clean, slanting bole is 4m long and hollow.

9 Wilmington 14x162+151(94) N. Two long clean hollow boles slant at opposite angles from a massive base; they are probably the healed halves of a single stem which split apart many centuries ago. The crown is very windswept but spreading.

10 Ninfield 12x169@0m(94) SE. The trunks, diverging from the base, are all so hollow that the tree resembles a kind of giant basket.

11 Stopham 12x242@0m(97) SW. The bole is covered in dense sprouts and does not seem to be hollow yet.

12 Herstmonceux 12x243@1.1m(97) SE. The bole - very swollen at the base and branching out at 1.2m - carries dense, wind-clipped sprouts, which were trimmed back in 1997. In 1835 the diameter was given as 218cm. Not hollow.

13 Ardingly 16x207@1.6m(97) S - taped underneath sprouts on a huge, rather decayed bole.

14 Bignor 15x189@0.3m(97)SE - with a long, clean, slanted bole.

15 Funtington 16x207(97) NE. The bole is sprouty and dead on the west side; the crown is particularly spreading.

16 East Chiltington 13x207@0.4m(94) NW. The bole is sprouty and burry and blocked up with concrete.

17 Chailey. Two trees S of church: 10x190@0.1m (sprouty and decayed) and 11x160@0.8m(94).

18 Stanmer. Two trees N of church: 12x179@0.5m (female) and 14x174@0.4m (male), both very hollow.

19 Slaugham 15x224(96) S - a clean, monumental trunk.

20 Etchingham 14x216(93) SE - very sprouty.

21 Wivelsfield 12x148(94) N - only half a trunk remains.

22 Walberton 16x184@0.5m(97) NW - a grand tree with a clean bole, not hollow. (There are old yews at Walberton and Warbleton, and at Warblington which is just over the Hampshire border, but not at Walderton.)

23 Ifield 12x184@1.3m(97) NE - a huge, sprouty bole, not yet hollow. It is possible that the village - "clearing with yew-tree" - was named after it.

24 Crowhurst 12x158(93) NW. Leaning, slightly hollow.

25 Amberley 12x154@0.4m(97) S - very sprouty; decayed on the east side.

26 Sullington 9x153@1m(97) SW - recently trimmed back.

27 Icklesham 11x147(94) N. With a clean, tapering bole, rather hollow.

28 Fittleworth 14x190@0m-0.6m(97) NW - a bushy tree, not yet hollow.

29 Eastbourne (St Mary's) 10x129@0.1m(94) SE - hollow and wizened.

30 Tillington 12x159@0m-0.8m(97) NW - bole divides into three.

31 Northchapel 11x150@0.4m(97) W - forks low down.

32 Warbleton 11x194@0m(94) E - branchy from the base.

33 Crowhurst 14x150@1.2m(93) SE. With a clean bole.

34 Westbourne. Eight trees forming a complete avenue from the lych-gate to the north door, all with striking clean boles and the largest slightly hollow (15x125@0.5m in 1997).

35 North Marden 11x188@0.1m(97) SW - branchy from the base.

36 Heyshott 9x165@0.3m(97) S - branchy from the base.

37 Bury 10x144@0.1m(97) by SE gate - forks low down.

38 Old Heathfield 11x131@0.9m(94) W - divides at 1m.

39 Wivelsfield 13x152@0.1m(94) S - branchy from the base.

40 Udimore 14x129@0.1m(94) S. The clean bole broadens with height.

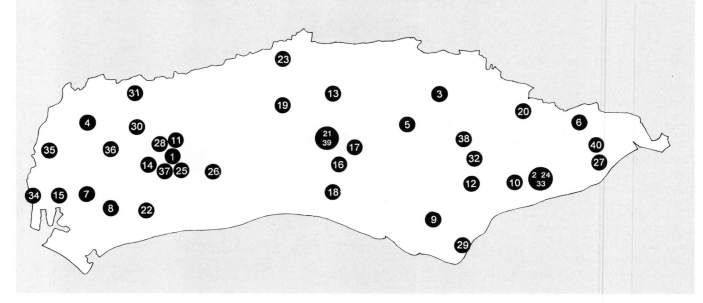

Caucasian Lime *T. x euchlora* Frequent in amenity plantings. Warnham Court (drive by Nursery House) 20x39(97); Wakehurst Place (S of Westwood Valley) 11x45(97).

Common Lime *T. x europaea* Until recently, abundantly planted everywhere. Stanmer Park (near house) 37x101(93); Petworth Park (hilltop beyond Upper Pond) 18x234(97); Cowdray Park: Lime Bottom, very sprouty, 32x243(95), E of Oaters Wood 35x188@1.2m(97); Buxted Park (in ancient avenue which largely blew down in 1987) 23x189@1.2m(94).

'Wratislavensis' Rare. Linton Gardens (p 1981?) 7x21(93).

T. intonsa At Wakehurst Place (Pergola): 8x**29**(97).

T. japonica Rare. Borde Hill (N edge of Little Bentley Wood, p1910) **13x42**(95).

T. mandshurica Rare. Borde Hill (N edge of Little Bentley Wood) 14x**45**@1.2m(95).

● *The Bratislava lime is the only lime with golden foliage, but it has yet to catch on*

Mutton-chop whiskers

The broad-leaved and small-leaved limes are both rare in the wild but the hybrid between them, the **common lime**, was until recently planted everywhere. Older common limes are eccentric characters with mutton-chop whiskers about the bole, and they grow biggest on the greensand. The avenue along Lime Bottom in Cowdray Park includes one tree whose diameter, taped between the whiskers, is the largest currently known, while another at Petworth is really an even bigger tree: its cleaner but very hollow trunk is reduced to two strips of living wood, which coalesce higher up. This is the big tree on the knoll beyond the Upper Pond in the vista from the house.

The small-leaved lime is a denizen of the acid soils of the Weald, least rare in the

Crawley area. To find a group of big coppice stools in a wood (as at Duckyls Wood near West Hoathly) is very unusual in Sussex; most trees survive singly in ancient hedge-lines.

Perhaps the biggest of all limes in Britain is a stately though hollow pollard, with a great spread, on the northern bank of the green lane east of Worth church, now the route of the Worth Way; it was first noted by Peter Bourne in 1993.

The broad-leaved lime (p. 15) is even rarer - its existence in the wild in south-east England was discovered by Dr Francis Rose only in 1989. (Botanists have long been adept at spotting and identifying tiny mosses and chickweeds: woods of 300-year-old trees, many 30m tall, are, of course, much easier to overlook.)

About a dozen native stands are now known, all on the scarp of the South Downs. At Rooks Clift, a wooded coomb above Treyford, nearly a hundred grey-trunked limes grow as tall and straight as beeches: a magical and liberating sight to anyone habituated to the quietly-repeating patterns of our common tree flora. As a wild population, these limes are unusual in growing taller and more gracefully than the cultivated broad-leaved limes which have been popular for so long in streets and parks.

Mongolian Lime *T. mongolica* Rare. Wakehurst Place (Coates Wood) 9x40(97).

Oliver's Lime *T. oliveri* Rare: large gardens. Wakehurst Place (drive to house) 10x57@0.3m(97); Borde Hill (outside Peartree Wood) 8x31(95).

T. oliveri x ?americana At Bishop's Palace (p1983?): 10x23(97).

T. paucicostata Rare. Borde Hill (Stephanie's Glade) 12x19++(96).

Broad-leaved Lime *T. platyphyllos* A rare native on the chalk, but long planted abundantly everwhere. St Roche's Arboretum (valley, mid) 37x97(97); Buxted Park (beside lake) 20x206(94); Leith Copse (wild tree) 36x96(97).

'Fastigiata' Occasional amenity tree. Penns-in-the-Rocks (behind house) **14x36**(94).

Cut-leaved Lime 'Laciniata' Occasional. Alexandra Park (duckponds bank) 17x41(93); Beauport Park (Oak Wood) 15x56(92).

'Orebro' At Stanmer Park (Arboretum, W edge, p1983): 9x17(95).

Red-twigged Lime 'Rubra' Rare? Stanmer Park (Arboretum, p1964) 16x44(95).

Vine-leaved Lime f. *vitifolia* At Alexandra Park (bank above bowling green): 19x**92**@1m(93).

Silver Lime *T. tomentosa* Occasional; becoming a popular amenity tree. St Cuthmans School (bridlepath N of school, superb trees) 32x114, 30x118(97); Pound Hill school 29x104(97); Worth Park Avenue, Pound Hill (largest) 27x118(97).

Silver Pendent Lime 'Petiolaris' Becoming frequent: parks and gardens. Staplefield Place 25x100; Lindfield pond (sickly; forks low) 21x142@1.2m(97); Varndean Close, Brighton (trimmed back) 22x109(94); Petworth Park (Upper Pond dam) 23x107(97).

T. tuan Rare. Borde Hill (Stephanie's Glade, "chinensis", p1933) 15x40(95).

● *The silver lime's white-backed leaves make it a strikingly ornamental big tree*

Californian Nutmeg *Torreya californica* Occasional in large gardens. Hollycombe: estate 16x68, gardens 15x52(97); Possingworth Manor (leaning at 45 degrees by 1997) x68(94); West Dean Gardens (Wild Garden) 14x68(97).

Japanese Nutmeg *T. nucifera* Rare: collections. Wakehurst Place (W of Slips) **14x35**(97).

Chusan Palm *Trachycarpus fortunei* In many large parks and gardens, and some small ones near the coast. Nymans (Top Garden) 10x21(96).

Trochodendron aralioides Occasional in large gardens. Chelwood Vachery 9x23(94).

Eastern Hemlock *Tsuga canadensis* Occasional as old tree. Hollycombe (estate) 25x104(97); Borden Wood 23x118@0.6m(97); Tilgate Park (Pinetum) 17x94@0.8m(96).

'Argentea' At Borde Hill (Gores Wood, much died back): **5x23**(96).

'Pendula' Rare. Sheffield Park (conifer walk) 7x38(94).

Carolina Hemlock *T. caroliniana* Rare. Hollycombe (garden) **13x45**(97); Leonardslee (Rhododendron Walks) 10x39++(96).

LIMES

NUTMEG TREES

HEMLOCKS

Chinese Hemlock *T. chinensis* Rare. Wakehurst Place (Pinetum) 10x26(97).
T. diversifolia Rare. Borde Hill: Warren Wood 14x25, Gores Wood 8x33@1m(95).
Himalayan Hemlock *T. dumosa* Rare. Borde Hill (Warren Wood) 11x32@1.2m(95).
Western Hemlock *T. heterophylla* Abundant - a plantation conifer. Wakehurst Place (Westwood Valley) 40x118(97); Malt House (Pinetum) 34x150(97); Borden Wood (forks) 39x125(97).
T. x jeffreyi Rare. Wakehurst Place (Westwood Valley) 16x35(97).
Mountain Hemlock *T. mertensiana* Occasional in large gardens. Wakehurst Place (Horsebridge Woods) 13x31(97); Eridge Park (Pinetum; p1900) 12x79@0.6m(94); Ely Grange (layering; p1902) 11x42++(94).
T. sieboldii Rare. Wakehurst Place: Westwood Lake 15x38, behind Sands Study Centre 12x49(97).

ELMS

• Elms with numbers are the offspring of deliberate crosses between disease-resistant forms, not yet named

Ulmus '148' Rare: in Brighton. Preston Park **24x63**(94); Crespin Way, Brighton 20x50(94).
U. '202' Rare: in Brighton. Crespin Way, Brighton 21x38(95); Sussex University (Refectory) 18x**50**(95); Longhill School (p1965) 16x49(94).
U. '215' Rare. Long Bridge Road (p1974?) **16x32**(97).
U. '240' Rare. Stanmer Park (Arboretum) **19x35**(93).
U. '260' Rare: in Brighton. Wildpark, Woodingdean (p1961) 17x56(94).
U. '297' Rare: in Brighton. Stanmer Park 20x37(94); Preston Park 18x40(94).
Wahoo Elm *U. alata* Rare: in Brighton. East Brighton Park **12x26**(94).
American White Elm *U. americana* Occasional. Stanmer Park (top of Arboretum, fine tree) 25x72(93); Buchanan Hospital (slowly dying 1998) 15x87(94).
'Exhibition' At Sussex University: **15x31**(94).
'Pendula' At Woodvale Crematorium (along drive): **30x68**, 23x79(93).
U. 'Christine Buisman' Occasional in Brighton. Sussex University (Refectory) 13x18(95); Carden Park 12x31(94).
U. 'Commelin' Occasional municipal plantings. Sussex University (Biological Sciences) 22x42(95); Brighton University (Falmer, p1966) 21x61(95); Windlesham House School 14x51(96); Rye Salts (best of three) 15x41(96); Hammy Avenue, Shoreham (S end, E side, leaning) 15x34(94).
U. 'Coolshade' Rare. Ryecroft (p1964) **19**x53(96); Tenantry Down Road, Brighton 15x**54**(94).
Coritanian Elm *U. coritana* v. *angustifolia* Possibly native; rare. Deans Road, Alfriston **25x80**(95).
v. *rotundifolia* Possibly native; rare. Hove Recreation Ground 16x45(95).
U. coritana x minor Rare. Round Wood 30x57, 28x58(95); Portland Avenue, Brighton 14x49(96).
U. 'Den Haag' Rare. Swanborough Drive, Brighton **17x45**(94).
U. x diversifolia Possibly native; rare. Holt Wood 23x76(95); road outside Lullington Court 21x77(93).
U. 'Dodoens' (494) Rare. Stanmer Park (Arboretum, p1982) 12x**20**(93).
U. x elegantissima Possibly native; occasional. Trinity Church, Eastbourne 19x56(95); Hartington Road, Brighton 16x58(94).
U. x elegantissima x minor In North Victoria Gardens: 7x16(96).

Immemorial elms

One day in 1986, when Peter Bourne was unemployed in Brighton, his attention was caught by the yellow autumn foliage of a tree in one of the town parks. This turned out to be an **elm**, the most threatened and least appreciated of Sussex trees. Peter, a Sahaj Yogi of American Indian descent, is never one for diluted enthusiasms, and he spent most of the next three weeks tramping the streets and recreation grounds of Brighton from dawn to dusk, finding more and more of these enigmatic trees and teaching himself little by little to recognise the tremendous variety of forms in which they grow here.

Peter Bourne is now an international authority on Ulmus, and most of the information in this part of the book is derived from his exhaustive research. At the time when the current DED epidemic struck, extraordinarily little was understood of the wild distribution of elms in the county. Ulmus minor, the smooth-leaved elm, has a regional variant which is one of the commonest native trees along the southern edge of the Weald from Glynde to Rye, yet the Sussex Plant Atlas records it simply as a rare, planted species. With its slender, glossy leaves, this elm is quite easy to identify; others are far harder, thanks to thousands of years' promiscuous hybridisation on the one hand and the self-perpetuation, on the other, of a myriad of distinct, infertile

clones. The lock elm, for instance, was first described from populations in the east Midlands, but a few similar trees grow wild in Sussex (there are the remains of a hedge-line near Hampden Park, though with atypically scabroid leaves); others, in streets and parks, have clearly been planted.

In the woods of the Cuckmere valley and the round and square plantations of Folkington Manor Farm, a few trees survive with the features of the Coritanian elm (described from East Anglia); others, Peter Bourne considers, are hybrids of it. Elms have also been deliberately hybridised around the world in the quest for DED-resistance, and a multitude of named clones have been tried out over the years by the very active parks department of Brighton Borough Council. With new, fast-growing forms still being planted, and with mature trees constantly at risk from DED, the county's elm population remains extraordinarily fluid.

Two elms carry the names of places in Sussex: 'Chichester Elm' is, or was, a dubiously distinct variant on the Huntingdon Elm, and 'Kidbrooke Elm' - a fastigiate form of U. minor - was, according to J. C. Loudon, named after Kidbrooke Park at Forest Row rather than Kidbrooke in south London, though he did not know that it had ever grown there.

The commonest elm in the Weald used to be the wych elm, which is more tolerant than most of an infertile soil and is happier

growing alongside other species in a wood. With its large leaves it recalls a lime, or, in sucker form, a hazel bush. It is vulnerable to DED, but the Scolytus beetles which transmit the disease only seem to feed on it as a last resort, so that a few inconspicuous and rather runtish trees have been able to hang on to life outside the DED control areas: there is a notable population around Elsted.

Many garden forms of wych elm exist - 'Camperdown' with its igloo of giant leaves; 'Horizontalis', with a branching pattern as stiffly graceful as the fingers of a Javanese dancer; 'Nana', the perfect bonzai dome; 'Lutescens', whose foliage gains in intensity through the season like a bonfire to become the most respendent of golden trees - there is an avenue of big trees along Dyke Road Place in Brighton; 'Exoniensis', with an electrocuted, blackened appearance; 'Serpentinei' with its serpents'-nest of writhing limbs. A 'Serpentinei' at the top of Church Road, St Leonards (p. 35) became such a local landmark that it was preserved for 14 years after DED killed it. 'Lutescens' and 'Camperdown' seem to be quite disease-resistant and are still sometimes planted.

The English elm (U. minor var. vulgaris), whose billowing cumuli played so vivid a role in the English farmed landscape, is unfortunately the most susceptible elm of all to DED; the only significant population of the southern form left in the world is believed to be that in the South Downs control zones,

Wych Elm *U. glabra* Native; abundant, but mature trees largely restricted to Disease Control Zones. Queens Park, Brighton 28x116(93); Elsted village 17x66(97).

'Atropurpurea' At Cottesmore St Mary's School: **18x51**(93).

Camperdown Elm 'Camperdown' Occasional in gardens. Chiddinglye 8x40(96); The Hoo 6x60(90); Denton Road, Eastbourne 5x54(94); Ely Grange 5x40(94); Worthing Crematorium 4x36(96); Denmans 3x33(97); West Dean Gardens (one of three) 3x30(97).

var. *cornuta* At Sussex University (southern Ring Road): 16x37(95).

var. *cornuta x minor* var. *plotii* In North Victoria Gardens: 10x20(96).

Exeter Elm 'Exoniensis' Occasional. St Roche's Arboretum (near bottom gate) 18x40(97); Dumbrell Court 13x33(88); Robin's Cottage 11x24.

'Horizontalis' Occasional in gardens. Royal Pavilion Grounds 7x86(93).

var. *latifolia* Rare. Surrenden Road, Brighton **16x44**(88).

Golden Wych Elm 'Lutescens' Occasional in gardens. Dyke Road Place, Brighton **18x76**(95); Mowden Prep School 14x60(95); A22 at Whitesmith, (next to "Flagstaff")14x50; West Itchenor House (paddock) 10x48(97); Buckingham Park 11x34(94); Cadborough (field, TQ901194) 10x32(96).

'Purpurea' In Cowley Drive, Woodingdean: **20x75**(88).

'Rugosa' In Kings Drive, Eastbourne: **15x51**(96).

'Serpentinei' Rare. Jevington church **7x32**(88).

U. glabra x laevis Rare. Brighton University (Moulsecoomb, p1964) **17x48**(95).

U. glabra x minor Native; occasional resistant wild populations, eg in Hastings. Hove Recreation Ground **26x89**(95); William Street, Bognor Regis 12x46(97); Laton Road, Hastings 20x80.

U. glabra x minor var *plotii* At Hove Recreation Ground: 11x54(95).

U. glabra x minor var. *sarniensis* In Eversfield Road, Eastbourne: **14x51**(93).

U. glabra x minor var. *vulgaris* At St Anne's Well Gardens: **27x104**(93).

U. glabra subsp. *montana x minor* In Royal Pavilion Gardens: 18x44(95).

U. 'Hamburg Hybrid' In Long Bridge Road, Lullington (p1974?): **10x27**(94).

U. x hollandica 'Bea Schwarz' Occasional in Brighton. Stanmer Park (Tennantslain belt) **20x37**(95); Lewes Road, Brighton 16x**38**(95); Crespin Way, Brighton 20x32(94).

Belgian Elm 'Belgica' Occasional in Brighton. Lawn Memorial Park 20x49, 19x65(94); Albourne Close, Brighton 19x44(94).

'Dauvessei' Rare. Highleigh **23**x71(94); Extra-mural Cemetery, Brighton 22x**78**(93).

'Daveyi' In Hove Recreation Ground: **17x64**(95).

'Groeneveld' Occasional recent municipal plantings. Barcombe Road, Brighton 15x40, 13x**42**(95); Stanmer Park (front of house) 15x38(93); Ardingly Recreation Ground 12x24(96); North Walls, Chichester 11x27(97).

Dutch Elm 'Hollandica' Frequent, at least in Brighton. Park Crescent, Brighton 34x96(94); Cedar Gardens, Brighton 25x**129**(93); Convent Field, Lewes 25x87, 23x87(94); Hartfield Square, Eastbourne 25x105(94); Tongdean Court (cut back) 23x124(95).

Wych elm

"Lofty"

Dutch elm

and even here there have been many losses. The English elm was relatively scarce in the Weald but its suckers are still abundant in the coastal plain and the western Downs. By 1997 these had reached 18m in Screens Wood near Arundel, and had begun to suffer a second wave of infection.

A thousand English and Dutch elms were planted around the Level in Brighton in November 1845 as a gift to the town from the Pelhams of Stanmer Park; 180 survived in 1995. In Preston Park are 'Lofty', an English elm of great symmetry and beauty which Peter Bourne maintains is the finest tree of any kind left in the south, and the 'Preston Twins', two squat and hollow giants which are probably the oldest remaining elms in Britain. Climb inside them, and the traffic roar on the Preston Road is suddenly stilled as the trees gather you into their own, long-lost world.

Botanically, English elm is probably a clone of the smooth-leaved elm, *U. minor*. Both are trees of farmland rather than woods, revelling in deep, rich soils and sunshine. Both carry cloudy masses of tiny leaves and intricate clusters of winter twigs. The wild *U. minor* population however is far more variable, with local forms showing evidence of past hybridisation (with wych elm in Hastings, for instance); English elm very seldom produces fertile seed, though Peter Bourne feels that a distinctive tree by the southern entrance to St Anne's Well

Gardens in Hove is hybrid between English and wych elms. The variability of the smooth-leaved elm population has meant that a few individuals around the county have inherited a degree of immunity to DED. One such tree at Selmeston, in the open plain of the eastern Low Weald, has two crooked coppiced trunks emerging from a huge burred boll. A remarkable 'sport' on the stream-bank above Station Approach near Horsted Keynes has large, glossy, yellowish leaves and is as slender as a Lombardy poplar (18x23 in 1998).

The spear-shaped wheatley elm, which was such a popular street tree in the 1920s and 30s, retains a dominant presence in Brighton and Eastbourne, where it is one of the last trees into leaf and always looks horribly dead in early May. This, in fact, is what sometimes enables it to hold out against DED: there are no young shoots to interest the first generation of bark beetles in spring. One in the Paradise Plantation, under the shelter of the Downs at the top of the Meads Golf Course in Eastbourne, is the tallest tree for many miles around. The old tree in St John's Road, near the Polegate level crossing, is another landmark; it suffered a branch-infection some years ago but this was spotted quickly enough for the tree to be saved. The finest of all are the specimens which march along the Preston Road side of Preston Park in Brighton. A few small, lopped trees still enjoy a life of sorts in downtown Bexhill; all

the plantings at Cuckfield are now gone.

'Wredei', a golden elm with twisted foliage and erect branches, also belongs in this group. It is one of the most disease-resistant forms and still gets planted in small gardens.

The Huntingdon elm, known only as a planted tree, is intermediate between wych and smooth-leaved elms: a magnificent vase of big, spring-green leaves which DED can only kill very slowly. The biggest now is outside the disease control zones, on top of the east embankment of the Cuckoo Trail just south of the edge of Hailsham; another at least 150cm in diameter had to be felled in 1990 at Manor Farm, East Lavant, and may have been an example of 'Chichester elm'. Younger cousins which have been planted outside the disease control zones in the hope that they will have even greater immunity are the rather similar 'Commelin' and the neat, glossy 'Groeneveld.'

Thanks to the Conservation Foundation's 'Elms Across Europe' initiative, the most widely-planted elm is now 'Sapporo Autumn Gold', a hybrid of Siberian and Japanese elms raised at the Sapporo Botanic Gardens in Japan - it is particularly conspicuous as a street-tree in Bexhill. It inherits the near-immunity of many oriental elms and is a dainty, light-green tree whose spreading twigs branch as geometrically as the patterns of parquet flooring. It would be sad, though, if we had to accept this as the substitute for all that we have lost.

'Hollandica' x *U. minor* In King Henry's Road, Lewes: **23**x75, 18x**96**(93).

Downton Elm 'Smithii' At Newman Middle School: 6x16(93).

Huntingdon Elm 'Vegeta' Occasional as a mature tree; common in Brighton. Friston Place (waterworks road) 30x78(97); Cuckoo Trail, Hailsham (TQ590083) 22x134(94); The Green, Southwick 19x84(94); Gensing Gardens 16x69(93); Cherry Orchard Road, Chichester 17x64(97); Pickwell (leans) 27x96(96); Grey's School 20x127@0.6m(89); Friston Manor 25x90(94); Wealden House (slender tree in wood) 29x80; Hartfield Square, Eastbourne 17x93(94).

Japanese Elm *U. japonica* 'Jacan' At Sussex University: **14**x26(95).

U. laciniata At Sussex University (southern ring road): **13**x22(95).

European White Elm *U. laevis* Rare. Stanmer Park (Arboretum, top, old tree) 24x44(93); Borde Hill (Stephanie's Glade, p1943) 15x26(95).

U. laevis x pumila At Preston Park (near church, p1928): **13**x**62**(95).

U. 'Lobel' ('454') Occasional as young tree. Royal Pavilion Grounds (p1983) **14**x25(93); East Street, Brighton 13x30(96).

U. 'Louis van Houtte' Now rare. Carden Park (p1958) **16**x47(88); Dyke Road Park (NE side) 14x**61**(95).

U. macrocarpa At Stanmer Park (Arboretum): **6**x**35**(93).

Smooth-leaved Elm *U. minor* Native in the east and locally abundant; much planted. Highcroft Road, Alfriston **31**x51(96); near Selmeston (TQ511069) 20x99+85(94); Stanmer Park (Great Wood by Arboretum) 28x93(93).

clone '1' At Brighton University (Moulsecoomb): **19**x49(95).

clone '28' At Preston Park: **18**x41(96).

Cornish Elm var. *cornubiensis* Possibly native; occasional as old tree. Preston Park (rose garden end) **30**x**96**(93); Square Wood 27x70(94).

var. *cucullata* Rare. Hove Recreation Ground **13**x**40**(95).

'Dampieri' Rare. Longhill School (p1965) 12x33(95); Brighton University (Falmer) 12x33(95).

f. *pendula* Possibly native; rare. Hartington Road, Brighton 15x**66**(94).

Lock Elm var. *plotii* Possibly native; rare. Holt Wood 21x31(96); Hartington Road, Brighton 15x64(94).

'Purpurea' Rare. Dyke Road Drive, Brighton **15**x**38**(95).

Wheatley Elm var. *sarniensis* Abundant street tree in Brighton and Eastbourne. Paradise Plantation **33**x72(94); Preston Park (biggest in line) 31x**122**(93); Hartfield Square, Eastbourne (cut back) 19x109(94); St John's Road, Polegate 23x118(93); Alfriston Tye 27x98(88); The Avenue, Bevendean 27x104(95); St Anne's Well Gardens (cut back) 24x107(95); Gildredge Park 22x80(94); All Saints Church Hall, Crowborough (pair) 21x64(97).

'Schuurhoek' At Stanmer Park (Tennantslain belt): **16**x49(95).

English Elm var. *vulgaris* Native; abundant, but mature trees restricted entirely to the Disease Control Zones. Friston Forest (Exceat Wood) **31**x85(96); Preston Park 14x**203**, 30x135(94); Milton Street (hollow) x150(94); Redman King House 20x105(94); Sussex University (Refectory) 16x132(94); Cedar Gardens 28x116(93).

Golden Elm 'Wredei' Frequent; still planted in small gardens. Blakers Park 12x47(94).

U. minor x var. *plotii* In South Victoria Gardens: 9x20(96).

U. minor f. *pendula x* var. *plotii* In Wilbury Road, Hove: **13**x**51**(95)

Chinese Elm *U. parvifolia* Occasional in large gardens. Royal Pavilion Grounds 12x35(93); Wakehurst Place (Coates Wood) 12x32(97); Fontridge Manor 8x23(95).

'Hokkaido' At Stanmer Park (Arboretum): **13**x28(93).

U. 'Plantijn' Occasional as young tree. Brighton bowling lawns 11x19(95); North Victoria Gardens 10x21(96).

Siberian Elm *U. pumila* Occasional. Brighton University (Falmer) 21x50(95); Long Bridge Road (p1974?) 18x60(97).

var. *arborea* Rare. Hove Magistrates' Court 13x29(89).

'Aureo-variegata' In Downsview Road, Seaford: **14**x**42**(97).

'Aurescens' At Stanmer Park (Arboretum): **12**x**21**(94).

'Dropmore' Rare. Tenantry Down Road, Brighton **17**x**50**(94).

'Hansen' Occasional as young tree. Stanley Deason High School 8x23, 7x**24**(96); East Brighton Park 6x17(90).

'Variegata' At Stanmer Park (Arboretum): **14**x**32**(94).

U. 'Regal' Occasional as young tree. Hangleton Way, Hove 9x17, 8x18(96).

Slippery Elm *U. rubra* Rare. Surrenden Road, Brighton **22**x**96**(95).

U. 'Sapporo Autumn Gold' Becoming a frequent amenity tree everywhere. Dog Kennel Barn 11x28(97); Wildpark, Woodingdean 11x21(94); Bexhill Down (Collington Lane East junction) 9x23(93); Sutherland Avenue, Bexhill 10x22(93); Fletching village 8x20(94).

Marn Elm *U. villosa* Rare. Stanmer Park (Arboretum, p1964) 16x40(93); Hodshrove Place 11x48(95).

U. x viminalis Probably native; rare planted tree. Larkrise Wood **23**x**50**(95).

'Marginata' At Balfour Middle School: 11x13(95).

Himalayan Elm *U. wallichiana* Occasional street tree in Brighton. Brighton University (Moulsecoomb) **19**x44(95); Longhill School 17x**57**(94); Birdham Place 15x50(95).

Californian Laurel *Umbellularia californica* Occasional in big gardens. Warnham Court 16x**122**@0.7m(97).

Viburnum cinnamonifolium Rare. Borde Hill (corner of old Kitchen Garden wall) 7x20++(95).

Caucasian Elm *Zelkova carpinifolia* Occasional: big gardens. Goodwood (High Wood) 21x63, 18x75(97).

Keaki *Z. serrata* Becoming a frequent amenity tree. Tilgate Park (mid S, fine tree) 21x86@1.2m(96); Lower Sherriff Farmhouse 19x**101**(97); Ashburnham (Burrage Wood near bridge, bushy) 18x126@0.3m(93).

Chinese Zelkova *Z. sinica* Rare. Alexandra Park (Thorpe's Wood, bushy, p1935) 15x41+(93); Stanmer Park (Arboretum, p1964) 10x29(94).

Z. 'Verschaeffeltii' At Wakehurst Place (drive to house): 8x41@0.6m(97).

Smooth-leaved Elm

• *The lock elm is named after the tendency of its tough timber to jam or lock a saw*

English Elm

• *The Chinese elm is a beautiful species with tiny glossy leaves and a flaking, orange bark*

• *The slippery elm's inner bark has long been used in America as a cough remedy*

• *The Californian laurel is known as the headache tree because of the painful effects of its aromatic foliage*

Keaki

Gazetteer

T his Gazeteer lists all the sites with notable trees featured in this book. All appearances in the list of outstanding trees are indexed. OS grid references are given where helpful. Forest Enterprise (FE) woodlands, most nature reserves and other sites as indicated, are open to the public. Where a private site is also known to open, this is stated, though detailed opening times have not been included as these may change from season to season. Some gardens may only open on one or two afternoons a year, often under the National Gardens Scheme (NGS) - full details of times and how to reach these gardens are published in the annual 'Yellow Book'. It is advisable to check that a garden is still open before you visit.

All other localities mentioned here - gardens, schools, hospitals, farms - are private, and often have only one tree of interest, which may simply have been noticed in passing. In all cases, permission must be obtained from the owner before you visit these sites.

Italicised page numbers refer to sites illustrated within the text.

The garden has been developed from a field since 1987. The trees include many rare *Eucalyptus* species and birches, some grown from original seed collections.
The grounds of the old house contain some mature rarities - survivors from many before 1987. The Sun Oak stands beside the lane at TQ202299.
The ancient deerpark has long contained many of the largest - and, in Oaters Wood, the tallest - native trees in Britain, notably sessile oaks. The garden also contains many superb trees, including an avenue (mixed ages) of wellingtonias.

The garden opens under the NGS while the park (containing a golf course) is criss-crossed with footpaths and recreation areas. A new arboretum is planned for the area between the Benbow Pond and the Queen Elizabeth Oak.
Collection of elms beside the railwayline (above Moulsecoomb station).
(permissive access). In the middle of a large conifer plantation, this collection of cypress cultivars was established in 1957-8 by the Castle Stewarts.
Big old conifers.
Ancient tulip tree, swamp cypress, etc.
This famous small garden is open most days.
The sheltered valley below Duckyls House (now in separate ownership) contains many rare trees planted over the middle years of the century.
Oak species on verge including two big Hungarian oaks.
Several big conifers; huge tulip tree in parkland.
The Saxon deer-park contains Britain's biggest beeches and is crossed by several footpaths and permissive paths. In the grounds of the house (NGS) is a line of eighteenth-century tulip trees, while, in the woods to the north, the Victorian pinetum (now very overgrown and inaccessible) still retains several of the county's tallest trees.
A notable group of trees, many planted by John McCarthy of Court Lodge. Most are labelled.
The old barns are sheltered by a grove of phillyreas.
Several trees of outstanding growth.
A chalk scarp woodland with groves of yew and whitebeam.
The park has now lost all its huge elms; one very rare tree is the Manchurian walnut near the footpath below the house.
(opens occasionally). The gardens and surrounding fields - even the farm muckheap - were converted into a very extensive arboretum by a previous owner, Mr. Watson, during the 1960s.
(public park).
(public park).
(open access to most of the grounds). Notable trees include the 1761 planting of cedars of Lebanon and the numerous old cork oaks.
The home of William Robinson, who popularised the "wild garden" in the 1890s; now a hotel. The gardens, beautifully maintained, are sometimes opened to the public. More trees were planted by Robinson around the lake and drive in Gravetye Forest (FE).
The celebrated gardens are open most days.

The gardens are on the site of a Victorian nurseries and there are several interesting specimen trees.
From 1903 to 1936, Wakehurst was the home of Gerald Loder (the brother of Edmund at Leonardslee and son of Sir Robert at the High Beeches). With its great Elizabethan house, lakes, and precipitous Wealden valleys ringed with natural sandstone outcrops, the estate was a superb setting for a tree collection second only to the Clarkes' at Borde Hill. In the 1960s, concerned that air pollution was making Kew an unsuitable site for many of its trees, especially conifers, the Royal Botanic Garden established Wakehurst Place as its country out-station, and the bluebell woods are now packed with many of the world's rarest and most endangered species. The National Collection of birches is held in Bethlehem Wood. Many of Gerald Loder's specimens survive to form the framework of the gardens, which are immaculately maintained.
During the middle years of the century the Lucas family established Warnham as another of the great Sussex gardens. The big house is now a school (which owns the much-depleted pinetum), while the Wild Garden, full of rare trees but long neglected, is currently being restored by Phil and Angela Lowe, who hope to open it to the public in due course.
(sometimes open).
(open daily, March to October, 11-5). The park and garden, which have had a long tradition of the cultivation of rare trees, have recently been beautifully restored by the Edward James Foundation. There are some notable rare oaks in the Wild Garden. The national collection of tulip trees is also held on the West Lawn. St Roche's Arboretum is 1km away on the trail across the old Park.
(Sussex Wildife Trust nature reserve).
The two great cedars were planted in 1761.
(public). There are some unusual trees beside the Lewes Road, at the northern end of this enclave of chalk downland and scrub in Brighton.
The park is notable for its rose gardens and lilac collection; there are several good young trees.
Notable elms; many younger trees.
A number of large roadside silver limes.
The Crematorium was developed on the site of the demolished Munton House, and incorporates a variety of large and rare trees which have grown well in this sheltered downland valley.

The sponsors of this book

It would have been impossible to produce The Sussex Tree Book
without the generous support of the following:

West Sussex County Council
East Sussex County Council
The Sussex Men of the Trees
Horsham District Council
Lewes District Council
Borde Hill Garden Trust
Hastings Borough Council
The Sussex Gardens Trust
The Edward James Foundation
The Tree Register of the British Isles

Index of English Tree Names

For trees with several common names, only the name preferred in the book is indexed here: eg. 'handkerchief tree' appears under 'dove tree' and 'mountain ash' under 'rowan'. Italicised page numbers refer to illustrations.

General Index

Photographic credits

All photographs in this book were taken by David Arscott, with the exception of the following, to whom grateful thanks:

Phil Belden p. 37
Neil Fletcher p. 28
David Harvey p. 32
Pam Johnson pp. 8, 35, 43, 51
David Saunders pp. 8, 19, 20 (top), 24, 39